JOINERY
AND CARPENTRY

VOLUME II

VOLUME II

DOORS, FRAMES, AND PANELLING

WINDOWS

BY

THOMAS CORKHILL, F.B.I.C.C., M.I.STRUCT.E., M.COLL.H.

GEOMETRY

BY

J. F. DOWSETT, A.I.STRUCT.E.

JOINERY
AND CARPENTRY

A PRACTICAL AND AUTHORITATIVE GUIDE
DEALING WITH ALL BRANCHES OF THE CRAFT
OF WOODWORKING

EDITED BY

RICHARD GREENHALGH

VOLUME II

SECOND EDITION
(*REPRINT*)

THE NEW ERA PUBLISHING CO., LTD.
45 NEW OXFORD STREET, LONDON, W.C.1

MADE IN GREAT BRITAIN AT THE PITMAN PRESS, BATH
E4—(T.5582)

JOINERY AND CARPENTRY
VOLUMES AND SECTIONS

PREFACE

THE first volume of *Joinery and Carpentry* dealt with tools, workshop practice, and joints ; and this, the second volume, goes on to explain the detailed construction of complete items of joinery work. The first section in this volume therefore treats of Doors, giving the methods of construction of the various types, hanging, and the finishings of the doorways.

Regarding the next section, it is often, and truthfully, said that no joiner or carpenter can be really proficient at his craft without a sound knowledge of Geometry. This subject consists of two parts, Plane Geometry and Descriptive (or Solid) Geometry. Under the heading of Plane Geometry, Mr. Dowsett touches on all the problems likely to be met with in practice ; but in addition he shows the reader how the solutions can be reasoned out, thus giving more interest to the subject, and putting less strain on the memory in remembering the solutions.

Descriptive Geometry is at the base of all the most difficult examples of joinery and carpentry, as handrailing, circle-on-circle work, and roof bevels. In this subject, it is of little use merely to be able to drawout the solutions ; the student must be able to picture the problems in space and understand why the various lines are drawn on his paper.

The concluding section of Volume II deals exhaustively with the construction of Windows. It treats of all the many types, including a brief description of metal windows, which are often fixed in a wood surround and therefore may be said to come partly in the province of the Joiner and Carpenter.

CONTENTS OF VOL. II

SECTION V

SECTION VI

SECTION VII

SECTION V

DOORS, FRAMES, AND PANELLING

BY

THOMAS CORKHILL, F.B.I.C.C., M.I.Struct.E.
M.Coll.H.

Formerly Lecturer in Building, Walthamstow Technical Institute
Silver Medallist Worshipful Company of Carpenters
Examiner to the Lancashire and Cheshire Institutes
and the National Union of Teachers

SECTION V

DOORS, FRAMES, AND PANELLING

DOORS

Varieties. Doors are classified as *ledged, ledged and braced, framed and ledged, panelled, solid,* and *flush.* The panelled door allows for much variation in the design and general treatment. The variation is usually in the formation of the panels and in the mouldings. Special types are cabinet, composite, double, dummy, dwarf, folding, fire-resisting, hatch, jib, revolving, sliding, stable, swing, trap, and warehouse.

Sizes. The dimensions of doors depend upon the requirements. The width of single doors for ordinary purposes may vary from 2 ft. 6 in. to 3 ft. 6 in. Standard sizes are 6 ft. 4 in. by 2 ft. 4 in. to 6 ft. 8 in. by 2 ft. 8 in. in 2 in. rises. Doors less than 2 ft. 6 in. wide are only suitable for cupboards.

Ledged Door. This door, which is often called a *batten,* or *barred,* door, is used for outbuildings and temporary work. It is the simplest form of door, and consists of boards, or battens, and three or four ledges. Fig. 1 shows the usual type. The boards are usually about 5 in. by $\frac{7}{8}$ in., but they are selected to *build up* the necessary width. They may be tongued and grooved, ploughed and tongued, or rebated. The joints are vee-jointed or beaded to relieve the plain appearance and to hide the open joints after shrinkage.

The **ledges** are about 5 in. by $1\frac{1}{2}$ in., and they may be chamfered or bevelled. For outside work they should be bevelled, as shown at *B,* to throw off the

1

water. The best form of ledge for weathering is shown
at *C*, which allows water to drip off at the throating.
The chamfers shown at *A* are only used for inside
work. To improve the appearance it is usual to return

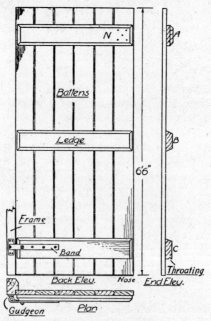

Fig. 1. Ledged Door

the chamfer or bevel on the ends of the ledges by means
of the trimmer machine. The ledges should be about
$\frac{1}{4}$ in. shorter than the width of the door, to allow for
shrinking and fitting.

Construction. The boards are selected to build up
the width. They are cut to length and cramped
together. The outer boards are marked so that any
surplus width is divided between them. If the boards

do not build up the width satisfactorily, all the boards should be reduced in width and re-grooved. The backs of the ledges should be *out of twist*. One of the chief faults of this type of door is its tendency to twist, or warp, and every precaution should be taken to avoid this defect.

When the battens and ledges are prepared, the position of the ledges should be marked on the back of one of the outside battens. The ledges should then be fixed securely to this outside batten, as shown at *N*, and square to the edge. Sometimes one or two screws are used for this purpose instead of nails, to prevent the outside batten from *lifting* away from the ledge. The batten is next turned over so that the three ledges lie perfectly flat and " out of twist " on the bench. The remainder of the battens are then placed in position on the ledges and cramped up. They are then nailed to the ledges with three or five nails placed zigzag. The nails should be driven in " on the skew," in opposite directions, for greater security. Sometimes the nails are selected longer than the combined thickness of ledge and batten, and then they are *clenched* on the back of the ledge. This is unsightly, but strengthens the nailing considerably. It is advisable to prime the tongues and grooves and the insides of the ledges, if not the whole of the timber, before assembling. The nails should be punched and the nail holes stopped after priming.

Ledged and Braced Doors. The ledged door has a tendency to drop at the *nose*, see Figs. 1 and 2, because the nails *give* after a time due to shrinkage of the timber, the corrosion of nails, and the banging of the door. To strengthen the door and to prevent the nose from dropping, *braces*, as shown in Fig. 2, are often used. The braces are the same size and section as the ledges, and the bottom end of the brace must be on the hinged side of the door, because, actually, the braces are " struts." The stuff should be seasoned otherwise the braces will fail in their purpose after shrinkage has taken place.

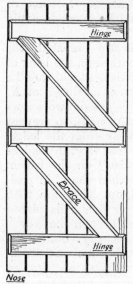

FIG. 2. LEDGED AND BRACED DOOR

It is usual to prepare the door as for a ledged door, and then to *let in* the braces. Two methods of " letting in " the braces are shown in Fig. 2 : either method is satisfactory. The brace should be kept back about $2\frac{1}{2}$ in. from the end of the ledge, to prevent the thrust from splitting away the small portion of the ledge. When the braces are fitted in position the battens are nailed to them in the same way as for the ledges.

Framed and Ledged Doors. This form of battened door, Fig. 3, has a better appearance than the two previously described. It is more rigid and better able to resist any change of shape, and is the best form of door for external positions where appearance is not very important. The framing consists of stiles, top rail, and ledges. Sometimes the bottom ledge is replaced by a rebated bottom rail which is the same thickness as the stiles and head. The stiles and head are usually 2 in. thick, but the ledges are 2 in. thick less the thickness of the battens. All the framing is flush on the back. The illustration shows half inside and half outside elevation. The rails should have a *through* chamfer, but the chamfers on the stiles are stopped.

The head is tenoned as for an ordinary panelled door, see Fig. 4, but the ledges have barefaced tenons. If the bottom rail is the same thickness as the stiles it should be prepared as shown in Fig. 5. The head and

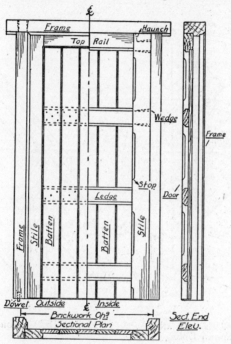

FIG. 3. FRAMED AND LEDGED DOOR

stiles are rebated for the battens, which run from the head to the floor. Sometimes, however, the stiles are ploughed for a tongue instead of being rebated; this is usually decided by the width of the boards available. The head should be beaded for beaded battens to break the joint. If the battens are vee-jointed both the head and stiles should be veed.

The framing is prepared and wedged up in the same way as a panelled door. It is cleaned off on both sides before the battens are nailed in position. Sometimes one wide ledge is used to serve as a lock rail instead

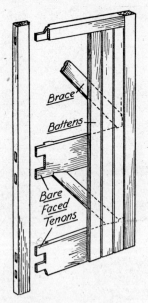

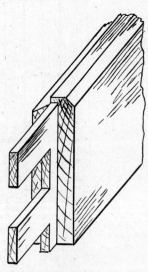

FIG. 4. FRAMED AND LEDGED DOOR

FIG. 5. DETAIL FOR BOTTOM RAIL

of the two inside ledges. Fig. 4 gives an isometric view of this type of door.

Braces may be added to the framed door if it is very wide or where extra strength is required. For ordinary conditions they are not necessary. The braces may be let in after the door is framed up, or they may be prepared with small barefaced tenons. They are usually placed so that the ends of the braces fit into the angle formed between the rail and stile, as shown for the top brace in Fig. 4. In this case the chamfers should be stopped on both stile and rail to avoid fitting the end of the brace with the chamfers. This method, however, is apt to force off the stiles, and it is better to let the braces into the rails, as shown in the bottom brace in Fig. 4; that is, similar to those shown in Fig. 2. When the braces are tenoned, as in Fig. 6, they entail much more labour in fitting, hence they are only used in good-class work. The detail shows the simplest method where the brace can be *let in* from the rebate side after the framing

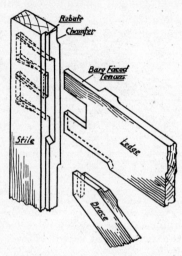

FIG. 6. DETAIL FOR TENONED BRACE

is wedged up. If the brace tenon which fits into the stile is made longer, it necessitates the braces being framed up with the remainder of the framing when wedging up. The tenon is then similar to a haunch on the rails, and makes a stronger job, but it entails too much labour for ordinary purposes.

Batten doors are usually considered inferior doors, and are made from the cheaper classes of timber.

DOOR FRAMES

The frame used for the foregoing types of doors, and for external doors generally, is shown in Fig. 3.

It is usually made from 5 in. or $4\frac{1}{2}$ in. by 3 in. deal. The rebate varies according to the door. Fig. 1 shows a $\frac{7}{8}$ in. rebate for a ledged door, and Fig. 3 shows a 2 in. rebate for a framed door. Sometimes the rebate is planted in inferior work, and proves an advantage when the ledged door is warped. For very cheap work the rebate is often omitted and the ledged door is

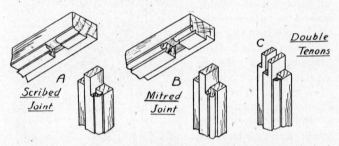

FIG. 7. DETAILS OF SOLID FRAME

hinged on to the face of the frame. In many districts the frames are called *casings*, and sometimes " solid frames."

The moulding may be omitted or it may be more elaborate than the example shown, according to the quality of the work. The usual moulding is an ovolo or a chamfer.

Details for Frame. The head runs through, and the joint between the post and head is a mortise and tenon joint. Fig. 7 shows several methods of making the joint. The usual method for an ovolo moulding is the scribed joint shown at *A*. When the moulding is a return bead, or if it is *undercut* in any way, it is necessary to mitre the moulding as shown at *B*. For very wide frames *double tenons* are sometimes used, as shown at *C* ; they help to keep the shoulders tight on the outsides. It is a common practice to make a slot mortise in the head, and to fix the joint by a hardwood pin or by nails, but the wedged joint is better.

The position of the rebate depends upon the type of door. For outhouses the rebate is generally on the outside, but for ordinary entrance doors the rebate is on the inside, so that the door opens inwards. Exit doors for public buildings open outwards, and the

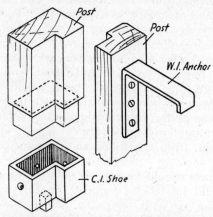

FIG. 8. CAST-IRON SHOE AND WROUGHT-IRON ANCHOR

rebates are thus on the outside. If there is no moulding on the frame, the shoulders on the post will be unequal in length. This applies also to stop chamfers and to slightly rounded corners. In the latter case a mason's stop is used for the round.

Fixing the Frame. For inferior work it is usual to erect the frame and to build the brickwork round it. This method saves considerable time, but it is not good for the timber, especially if it is inclined to be sappy. The better method is to complete the brickwork, and to fit and fix the frame when the moisture has evaporated, to a large extent, from the brickwork. The best fixing is provided by inserting plugs at convenient distances apart and then to nail the frame to the plugs. Pallets built into the joints as the brickwork is erected are good substitutes for plugs. Breeze bricks that will hold the nails are also satisfactory, but wood nogs are not good.

The feet of the posts should be dowelled into the step, or threshold, see Figs. 3 and 4. The iron dowels may be round or square, as explained in "Fastenings." Cast-iron shoes are often used for fixing the posts to concrete thresholds. Fig. 8 shows the usual type; it is provided with a square dowel cast on to the shoe. The shoe preserves the foot of the post, as it prevents the moisture from the concrete being absorbed by the timber. One or two holdfasts along each post also help to secure the posts. In exceptional cases bolts may be used, or wrought-iron anchors, as in Fig. 8. The latter project 9 in. from the frame to engage with a brick joint.

The frames should be primed before they are fixed. They should be bedded against the brickwork with hair mortar, or with oil putty. When the latter is used it is advisable to give both the frame and the brickwork a coat of boiled linseed oil, and to fix the frame as soon as the oil is *tacky*.

Fanlights. It is usual to provide a fanlight to door-frames for external walls, as shown in Fig. 9. The hinged sash above the door provides both light and ventilation. If the latter is not required the sash may be fixed; but it is then usual to dispense with the sash and to fix the glass into the rebate in the frame. The sash may be pivoted, but it is usual to hinge it to the transome, as shown in Fig. 9. A further explanation will be given in the section on "Windows."

The sash would be opened with a fanlight opener. *Hoppers* may be provided at the sides to prevent draughts. These are simply triangular pieces of wood about ¾ in. thick with a projecting bead on the edge for the sash to rest on when it is open. The hoppers are fixed to the frame, and they may be any width at

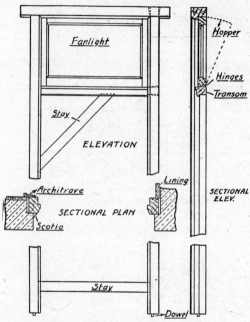

Fanlight

Hopper

Stay

Hinges

Transom

ELEVATION

Lining

Architrave

SECTIONAL PLAN

SECTIONAL ELEV.

Scotia

Stay

Dowel

FIG. 9. FRAME WITH FANLIGHT

the top to suit the amount of opening required for the sash. The transome receives the door and also the hinges for the light. It should be beaded as shown, to break the joint and to receive the hinges.

Finishings. The sectional plan shows one side of the frame finishing flush with the plaster, with an architrave breaking the joint between the plaster and the frame. The other side shows the jamb continued beyond the frame and a lining to build up the width. The lining may be any width to suit the thickness of the brickwork, and it may be plaster instead of wood. The stays are only temporary ; they are required to

FIG. 10. BAND AND GUDGEON

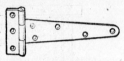

FIG. 11. "T" HINGE

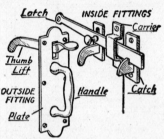

FIG. 12. THUMB LATCH

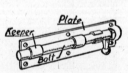

FIG. 13. TOWER BOLT

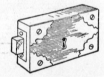

FIG. 14. STOCK LOCK

keep the frame square and rigid until it is fixed in position. A scotia is usually planted round the outside of the frame to cover the joint between the brickwork and the frame.

FURNITURE FOR BATTEN DOORS

Hinges. Ledged doors are hung by *bands and gudgeons* when the hinge is on the ledged side of the

FIG. 15. VARIOUS ARRANGEMENTS OF PANELS

door, as in Fig. 1. The usual type of band and gudgeon, sometimes called a strap hinge, is shown in Fig. 10. The band has usually three screw holes and one bolt hole. Heavy bands may have all the holes prepared for bolts. The length may be anything above 9 in., according to the weight of the door. The gudgeon is usually a *plate gudgeon* when it can be fixed to a wooden frame, but they can be obtained to drive into the frame. When they are fixed in masonry they are made dovetail in shape and ragged, and *run in* with molten lead. For brickwork they have two *spread anchors* to engage with the brick joints, or the gudgeon is continued as a bolt to pass through the wall.

When the hinge is on the batten side of the door, a *cross-garnet*, or " T " hinge, is used. (See Fig. 11.) Exceptions occur in both cases; for instance, the cross-garnet could be used for Fig. 1, by fixing a packing piece on the frame equal in thickness to the ledge. Sometimes the hinge is not placed on the ledge, but the battens alone do not give a secure fixing for the screws. The bands also can be placed on the batten side of the door when the ledges are inside. This requires the band to be turned round; and if necessary, to crank or bend the band a little, so that it fits to the door. Every case must be considered on its merits; but where strength is required the band is preferred. One or more bolts should be used for both types of hinges as these doors are generally subjected to rough treatment.

FASTENINGS

The Norfolk Latch. Fig. 12 is the usual type of fastening for ledged doors. It is often called a *thumb latch*, and sometimes a " Suffolk " latch. The plate carrying the handle and thumb lift is screwed on the outside of the door. The latch, catch, and carrier, or keeper, are fixed on the inside. The latch, which is operated by the thumb lift, slides in the carrier and engages with the catch which is fixed to the frame.

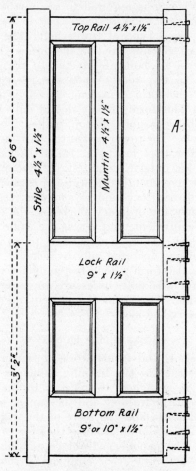

FIG. 16. FOUR-PANELLED DOOR

For inferior work the handle and thumb lift are omitted, and a hole about $1\frac{1}{2}$ in. diameter is bored through the batten, so that the finger can operate the latch.

Bolts. When it is required to secure the door from one side only, a *tower* or *barrel bolt* is used. Fig. 13 shows the usual type of tower bolt. The bolt slides into a socket which is fixed on the frame. The *keepers*, which control the bolt, are riveted to the plate which is screwed to the door. When the keepers are continuous in the form of a long barrel, it is called a *barrel bolt*. This form of bolt should only be made of brass, as the corrosion of iron makes it difficult to slide the bolt. The tower bolt is the best for outhouses.

Locks. The *stock lock*, Fig. 14, is the usual type of lock used for outside doors, stable doors, and other positions where metalwork quickly corrodes. It is a strong hardwood lock and is very serviceable, but it is too clumsy for ordinary purposes. A *dead lock* is the metal equivalent, and serves the same purpose as the stock lock. There is no handle to either of these locks ; they are operated only by a key.

Padlocks also form a good fastening for this type of door, where it is only necessary to secure the door from one side. This form of lock requires a hasp and staple to carry the lock.

Panelled Doors

For superior, and inside work, it is usual to panel the doors ; that is, the framing, which is of uniform thickness, is ploughed to receive thinner material. The details of the framing and the panels depend upon the class of work, and the taste of the designer. The treatment is nearly unlimited, as the following examples will show. The panels need not be rectangular ; very often they are circular or elliptical, especially above the lock rail ; and the top panels are often of glass instead of wood. Panel doors are generally distinguished by naming them according to the number of panels they contain.

Four-panel Door. The most common type is a four-panel door, as shown in Fig. 16. The illustration shows the approximate sizes for a 6 ft. 6 in. by 2 ft. 6 in. door, with panel moulding throughout. Stile A shows the position of the tenons, and the condition of the door after it has been wedged up. The surplus length on the stiles, which is called the *horn*, is left on until the door is fitted to the frame, to protect the corners.

The position of the lock rail varies considerably according to the design, especially for external doors. The panels are from $\frac{3}{8}$ in. to $\frac{1}{2}$ in. thick for ordinary purposes; but it is usual to make them from ply-wood, because it is stronger and does not shrink. The plough groove for the panels should be $\frac{7}{16}$ in. or $\frac{1}{2}$ in. deep. The details of construction are shown in Fig. 17.

Other arrangements for the panels are shown in Fig. 15, but there may be any number of panels up to nine, or even twelve for large entrance doors. The construction is practically the same in all cases.

Door with Frieze Rail. The addition of a frieze rail gives a more imposing appearance to the door, and it is generally introduced when the door is more than 6 ft. 8 in. in height. Fig. 17 is an isometric view of this type of door showing the details of construction, which apply generally to panelled doors. The various members are named on the drawing for the convenience of reference. The double tenons on the lock rail receive the mortise lock as previously explained. All the joints have been shown and explained in the section on " Joints." The muntins are stub-tenoned into the rails ; and the top and bottom rails are haunched for

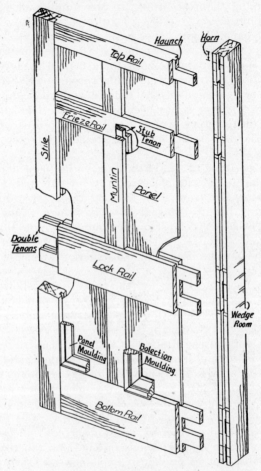

FIG. 17. PANELLED DOOR (ISOMETRIC VIEW)

secure wedging. Two different forms of panel moulding are shown. One stile has been removed to show the method of " setting out " the stile for the rails. The drawing is " broken " in several places to show the method of forming the joints.

Setting Out of Panelled Door. A four-panel door and solid frame have been selected to illustrate the method of *setting out*. A more general description will be given in the section on " Setting Out." The door and frame should be set out, full size, on a board which is called a *setting-out rod*. The drawings should be

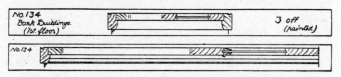

FIG. 18. ROD FOR DOOR AND FRAME

just sufficient for another person to be able to carry out the work. Too much detail is confusing, and serves no useful purpose. Any detail should only be given once, as it is assumed that the joiner doing the work is conversant with the general procedure. The drawings on the rod are the sections of the various members in their respective positions, as shown in Fig. 18. The illustration shows both sides of the rod ; one side showing the sectional plan and the particulars of the job, and the other side showing the sectional elevation. The rod is numbered and gives the name of the job, the position of the work, and the required number of the particular piece of work.

Setting Out the Rod. The openings are marked on the rod and then the margin is decided upon. In this case a scotia is planted round the opening after the frame is fixed, therefore the margin is arranged to take the scotia and to allow for irregularities in the brickwork.

A $\frac{7}{8}$ in. scotia will require, say, a $1\frac{1}{4}$ in. margin.
The next step is to draw the section of the frame.
If, however, the door is of any standard size, then the
door will be the chief consideration, and the section
of the frame and the margin must be modified to suit
the size of the door. Usually, all these conditions have
been considered before the brickwork openings were
formed, and the openings made according to the
requirements.

It will be noticed that only one panel is shown in
each view. Two lines are sufficient for the remainder.
One line shows the edge of the material to obtain the
lengths of the rails and muntins ; and the other line
shows the depth of the plough groove to obtain the
position of the mortises and the sizes of the panels.
The sections of the panel moulding and of the bolection
moulding are shown once only. That implies the same
treatment throughout the door. Any unusual features
must be shown distinctly, but for the ordinary type of
door the details on the rod in Fig. 18 are quite sufficient.
When the moulding is stuck on the solid it is necessary
to show the depth of the moulding in the setting-out,
in the same way as for the plough grooves ; this is to
obtain the lengths of the rails and muntins.

Cutting List. When the setting-out is completed it
is necessary to *take off* the materials required. Most
firms have printed forms on which the list of materials
is tabulated. Opposite is shown one kind of form,
but there are many variations. The last six columns
are for office use only.

At least one carbon copy, in addition to the original
list, is required. Some firms require two carbon copies ;
so that the office, the setter out, and the machinist
each has a copy for reference when required. The
machinist's copy accompanies the stuff through the
various departments—saw-mill, machine shop, and

CONTRACTORS, LTD., LONDON

No. of Rod..................134..........

Date...............8/12/50..................

Name of Job ....*Bank Buildings*..................................

Description of Work..............................3 *Panelled Doors and Frames* (1*st floor*)...............

No. of Pieces	Description	Wood	L.	B.	T.	Finished Sizes		Cube	Cut	Rate			
						B.	T.						
			ft. in.	in.	in.	in.	in.				£	s.	d.
6	Stiles (Fr.) . .	Yellow Deal .	6 11	5	3	$4\frac{3}{4}$	$2\frac{7}{8}$						
3	T. Rail (Fr.) .	„ „ .	3 6	5	3	$4\frac{3}{4}$	$2\frac{7}{8}$						
6	Stiles (Door) .	Yellow Pine .	6 10	5	$1\frac{1}{2}$	$4\frac{7}{8}$	$1\frac{3}{8}$						
3	Heads . .	„ „ .	2 $8\frac{1}{2}$	5	$1\frac{1}{2}$	$4\frac{7}{8}$	$1\frac{3}{8}$						
6	L. and B. Rail .	„ „ .	2 $8\frac{1}{2}$	10	$1\frac{1}{2}$	$9\frac{7}{8}$	$1\frac{3}{8}$						
3	Munt. . . .	„ „ .	2 –	5	$1\frac{1}{2}$	$4\frac{7}{8}$	$1\frac{3}{8}$						
3	Munt. . . .	„ „ .	3 3	5	$1\frac{1}{2}$	$4\frac{7}{8}$	$1\frac{3}{8}$						
	Bolection Mld. .		82 –	$2\frac{1}{2}$	$1\frac{1}{8}$	From	stock						
	Panel Mld. . .		81 –	2	$\frac{3}{4}$	From	stock						
6	Panels . . .	Yellow Pine .	3 –	10	$\frac{1}{2}$		$\frac{3}{8}$						
6	Panels . . .	„ „ .	1 10	10	$\frac{1}{2}$		$\frac{3}{8}$						

A TYPICAL CUTTING LIST FORM

joiner's shop. The rod also accompanies the stuff, and often the detail drawings in addition.

It is important that the cutter-out, or sawyer, should know the position of the work, so that he can decide whether the material is satisfactory for its position, and select it to the best advantage. This also applies to the machinist, because no alteration is possible after he has prepared the material. In the large shops the stuff is ready for cleaning up and assembling when it leaves the machinist.

The joiner has far more responsibility in the smaller shops. He is supplied with the rod and the planed-up material, and he has to set out the material from the rod for the machines—mortising, tenoning, moulding, etc. These processes will be explained in the section on " Machines." As these conditions present the most difficulties to the joiner, the following description of the procedure is given in detail.

Setting Out the Stuff. Select the material so that defects are hidden, and good figure is shown to the best advantage. Mark the face side and edge plainly to avoid mistakes. Set out one stile for the top, bottom, and lock rails. The required lines on the rod are first transferred to the face edge of the stile. These lines, which show edge of stuff and depth of plough grooves, are squared across the edge and then the positions of the mortises are marked. The mortises are next squared over to the back edge and the wedge room is marked. All these lines are shown on the detached stile in Fig. 17.

The stiles are arranged *in pairs* and placed on the bench, resting on two bearers *b*, as shown in Fig. 19. The stile that has been set out as a pattern is shown at *a*. It should be placed in the middle so that any discrepancy in squaring across the stiles will be modified. The lines are next squared over all the stile edges.

The illustration shows this operation being performed for the bottom rail.

When there is a large number of stiles, it is usual to set out *one pair* of them. All the stiles are then arranged in pairs with the two " set out " stiles on the outsides. The stiles are placed on their back edges on the bench, and cramped together at the ends. The lines are squared across the face edges with a straight-edge ; and then the stiles are turned over, in the

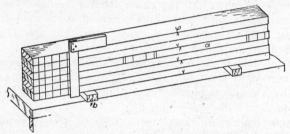

Fig. 19. Setting Out Door Stiles

cramps, so that the back edges can be marked. This method ensures that all the stiles will be set out exactly the same.

Gauging. Select a mortise chisel, which should be one-third of the thickness of the stuff. Set the mortise gauge to the chisel and at the centre of the material, and gauge the mortise holes on both edges of the stiles, *from the face side.*

Rails and Muntins. It is only necessary to set out one rail as a pattern when a tenoning machine is available. When the rails are prepared by hand they must all be set out, as explained for the stiles. The same remarks apply to the muntins. An allowance must be made for the shrinkage if the material is not well seasoned. This applies especially to the muntins. A lock rail may easily shrink $\frac{1}{8}$ in. during second seasoning. Experience is the only guide as to the amount to allow for shrinkage.

The mortises in the rails are set out after the tenoning is completed. When they are mortised on a machine, a stop can be arranged so that the rails can be mortised from the pattern, instead of setting out all the rails.

Preparation. When the mortising and tenoning have been completed, the stuff should be ploughed for the panels ; this may be done on the spindle or with a " drunken " saw. At the same time a *mullet* should be prepared ; this is a short piece of stuff used for testing the thickness of the panels when they are being cleaned up, as shown in Fig. 20. The tenons are then cut to width on the circular saw ; and the waste wood is removed by the tenon saw for the outer haunchings, and by a pad saw for the inner haunchings on the lock and bottom rails. (See Fig. 17.)

Lock Rail. The lock rail presents the greatest difficulty if it is prepared with double tenons. The " hand " method has already been explained in the section on " Joints." The tenoner will remove the core between the tenons, or a " drunken " saw may be used. Sometimes the joiner runs them up on the circular saw, which leaves very little to remove with the chisel.

Fig. 21 shows three different methods of preparing lock rails. The usual method is shown at *A*. The barefaced tenons *B* are used for batten doors where the battens run over the rail. The double tenons *C*, are only used on thick doors which have to be fitted with mortise locks.

Second Seasoning. The door framing is next loosely knocked together, usually without the muntins, and placed in a warm, dry room to allow the stuff to season. This is known as *second seasoning*. The length of time allowed depends upon the material, its condition, and the importance of the job. It may vary from one week to several months. In many cases the doors are framed up as soon as the building, for which they are intended, is started, especially if the doors are of pitch pine or hardwood.

The panels should be seasoning at the same time, but they are not cleaned up and mulleted until they

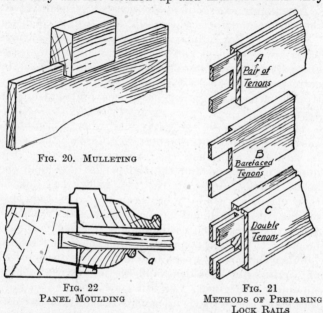

FIG. 20. MULLETING

FIG. 22
PANEL MOULDING

FIG. 21
METHODS OF PREPARING
LOCK RAILS

are required for assembling. The muntins may be used as skids between the doors, which should be stacked horizontally, and skidded so that there is a free access of air to all parts. Every precaution should be taken to prevent the doors from warping.

Panels. The panels should be cut to size so that there is a clearance of about $\frac{1}{16}$ in. all round. It is necessary to mullet them to ensure that they will enter the plough grooves easily. The sharp corners should be removed all round to prevent them from bruising the corners of the grooves. If the panels are too wide, they will burst off the stiles when expansion takes place. Most jobs are damp, and this soon affects a well-seasoned door.

Assembling. In good class work it is usual to fit the various members separately, and to test them for " winding." For ordinary work, however, the various parts are assembled and the door is cramped up. If any particular part requires to be adjusted it must be corrected, but usually the parts assemble without any trouble, especially if they have been prepared on the machines.

The following is the procedure when assembling. Insert the muntin into the bottom rail, place the panels in position, and then the lock rail. Place the top muntin in position and the top panels, and then the head. Finally, drive on the two stiles. The door is then placed horizontally on the bench. It should rest on bearers and should be perfectly " out of wind." If the door is twisted the shoulders and tenons should be eased to allow the cramps to pull the door straight.

When the door has been tested the stiles are knocked off, and all the shoulders, and the tenons near to the shoulders, are glued. The stiles are knocked up and the door is cramped up and wedged. The wedges should be dipped in glue. The tenons should not be glued at the outer ends, so that if the stile shrinks it will still hold to the shoulders. When driving in the wedges it is advisable to drive the outer wedges " in advance " of the inner wedges for the top and bottom rails. This tightens up the shoulders of the muntins. The door is now put on one side until the glue hardens. It is then cleaned up and moulded.

Moulding the Panels. The usual method of moulding

a panel is shown in Figs. 16 and 17. Either a panel moulding or a bolection moulding may be used ; the latter gives a better appearance, and is usually adopted for better-class work. It is advisable to cut the mouldings from one length continuously round the panel. This ensures a better intersection at the mitres ; except for the closing mitre, which should be placed in the least prominent position. Small mouldings are cut to the correct length in the mitre block. This is too laborious for large mouldings, which are usually mitred with the circular saw, on a sliding fence. In this case they are cut slightly longer than required, and trimmed to length on the trimming machine.

Bolection mouldings for good-class work that have to be polished or varnished, are often fixed by slot screws. The screws are inserted from the back of the panel, and a small panel moulding covers the screws and slots. The panel moulding, if nails are not permissible, is then glued to the framing. This gives freedom to the panel for contraction or expansion. Any form of moulding must be fixed free of the panels ; the nails must be driven into the framing only. Otherwise the panels may split when they shrink. To avoid bruising the moulding when driving in the nails, it is best to slide the hammer head along the blade of a try square. Panel pins are the best for fixing the mouldings, as they have no head, practically, to disfigure the mouldings.

Small mouldings are placed in position on three sides and then the fourth piece is sprung into position. A *slight* bevel on the back edge, as shown in Fig. 22, tends to keep the inside edge of the moulding tight to the panel. There is sometimes a tendency for the edge *a* to lift away from the panel. Even on bolection mouldings this bevel also is useful, as it tightens up the mitres when the mouldings are driven into position.

A small arris should also be planed off the corner of the bolection moulding, as it is too large to spring into position. This makes it easier to start the mouldings into position, and prevents bruising the corners. The four pieces should be *tapped* down into position simultaneously. Fig. 22 illustrates these hints slightly exaggerated.

MISCELLANEOUS PANEL MOULDINGS

Framed Mouldings. Hardwood bolection mouldings are often framed up and inserted as a whole frame, when the door framing is assembled. The mitres are fixed together by slip feathers, screws, and glue. The chief advantage of this method is that the mitres will not open when shrinkage takes place. They are also free of the framing and panels, so that any movement of the panels or framing will not disturb the moulding. (See Fig. 23.)

Another method is shown in Fig. 24. The chief advantage of this method is that the panels and mouldings can be completed whilst the framing is second seasoning, thus speeding up production. In this case the panel is framed up in the moulding, and then the whole is placed in position when the framing is assembled.

Solid Mouldings. This term is applied to mouldings that are stuck on the framing, instead of being planted. An example is shown by isometric projection in Fig. 25, and another by a section at *B* in Fig. 26. A door moulded in this manner requires more care in the preparation of the framing, when it is made by hand, than the door with planted mouldings. All the internal angles require to be mitred or scribed according to the type of moulding employed. It is very common to stick the moulding *on the solid* for machine-made doors, because the scribing is done at the same time as the

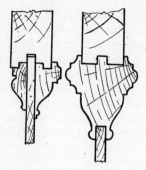

FIGS. 23 AND 24. FRAMED MOULDINGS

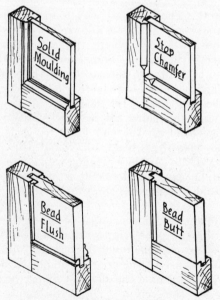

FIG. 25. PREPARING PANELS

tenoning. For hand-made doors, however, this method involves too much labour for general use.

The Stop Chamfer, Fig. 25, is very often used for panelled framing. No special preparation is required for the joints; and if the stops are left as they come from the machine, this method of "moulding" the panels entails less labour than any other method.

Beaded Panels. Sometimes it is required to increase the thickness of the panels to make them stronger. The panels are usually flush with the framing on one side, while the other side appears like an ordinary panel, and may be panel moulded or stop chamfered. Two methods of preparing panels of this description are shown in Fig. 25, and a section is shown in Fig. 26.

Bead Butt. The cheapest way is to bead the edges of the panels only. This is known as a *bead butt*, and appears unsatisfactory where the end grain of the panels meets the rails. Sometimes the ends of the panels and the rails are veed to break the joint.

Bead Flush. A more satisfactory method for appearance is the *bead flush*. In this case the bead is continued round the panel. It is impossible to make a satisfactory bead on the end grain, so it is usual to mitre and *plant* the bead all round the panel, as shown in Fig. 25. As these beaded panels are generally only used on external doors, it is necessary that the beads should be painted before fixing them round the panels.

Raised Panels. Another way of strengthening and ornamenting the panels is to raise them as shown in Fig. 27. This entails much labour but adds greatly to the appearance of the door. The illustration shows the method of forming the slots for fixing the bolection moulding by slot screws. The screw holes near the centre of the panel do not need slotting. The raising on the panel may be varied in many ways. The usual method is shown at *A*, but an alternative very often used is shown at *B*. This is a *fielded* panel.

Glass Panels. The top panels of doors are very often of glass. They usually add to the decorative effect

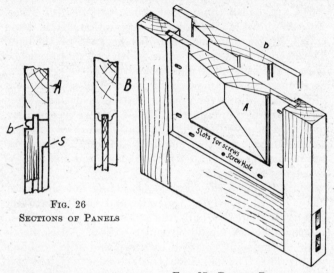

Fig. 26
SECTIONS OF PANELS

Fig. 27. RAISED PANEL

in addition to providing light. The glass may be ornamented in many ways. It may be coloured or embossed, or it may be formed by leaded lights. The latter is very effective if carefully selected. Very often the glass panel is circular or elliptical in shape. The simplest way of preparing for glass panels is to stop the plough groove at the lock rail and to leave the stiles square above the lock rail. A planted moulding is mitred round the top panel, or panels, to form a rebate for the glass.

Other Varieties of Panelled Doors

Diminished Stiles. When the upper panels are of glass it is usual to decrease the width of the stiles above the lock rail. This not only increases the lighting area but also improves the appearance of the door. The stiles are called diminished stiles, or *gun-stock* stiles. Fig. 28 shows a door of this description. It is often called a *sash door with margins* because of the bars. The head is usually the same width as the diminished part of the stile. The glass may be of one large square or it may be ornamented by bars. The arrangement of the bars allows for great variation in design. They may be straight or curved, and they may be rectangular, or placed diagonally. The illustration shows a common arrangement. All the members above the lock rail are moulded and rebated for the glass, and a *glass bead* is used to fix the glass.

Fig. 29 shows the method of setting out the stiles. They are mortised for the rails and then cut to the line *a*. If there are bars, the stiles should be mortised for them before moulding and rebating. An isometric view of the joint between lock rail and stile is shown in Fig. 30. The bevel on the shoulder requires care when setting out. A common error is to run the bevel to the top edge of the rail instead of allowing for the *sticking* of the moulding. The correct method is shown at *a* in Fig. 29.

The moulding between the lock rail and stile may be mitred ; but it is better scribed, so as to allow for shrinkage which may take place in the rail. An *apron moulding* is generally fixed on the lock rail, for ornamentation. Fig. 31 shows half the elevation of the usual type of apron moulding, and a vertical section through the lock rail. Examples are also shown in Figs. 37 and 80.

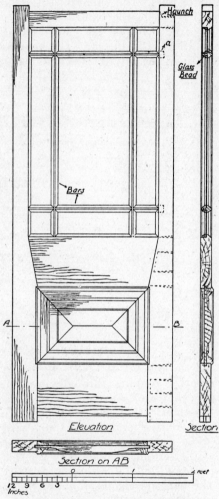

Elevation

Section

Section on AB

Fig. 28. Door with Diminished Stiles

Preparation of Bars. The bars are stub-tenoned into the framing, but where the bars intersect each other several alternative methods may be used. The best method is shown at *A* in Fig. 32. The bars are halved and the mouldings are mitred. The halving should be

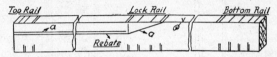

Fig. 29. Diminished Stile

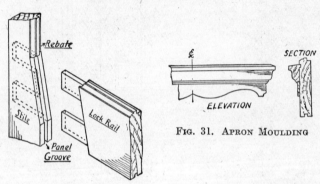

Fig. 30. Joint of Lock Rail

Fig. 31. Apron Moulding

on the line of the rebate. It is best to have the horizontal members "running through" on the rebate side, otherwise they are easily broken off when glazing.

Another method, often called *franking*, is shown at *B*. It is a mortise and tenon joint with scribed moulding. It is usually adopted where machines are available, as the scribing is done with the tenoning on the machine, and saves a lot of labour. When the corners of the bars are *slightly* rounded, as at *C*, it is usual to form a *mason's stop*, or mitre, as shown at *a*. The *stop* is formed when cleaning up the door, after

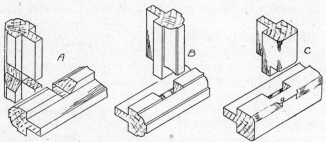

FIG. 32. PREPARING BARS

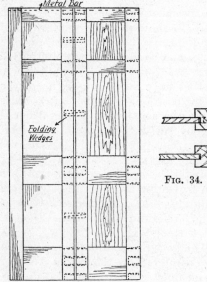

FIG. 33. DOUBLE-MARGIN DOOR

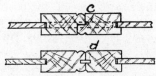

FIG. 34. DETAILS FOR STILES

it is wedged up. A large round should be mitred in the usual way, as shown at *A*. It is not suitable for scribing.

Double Margin Doors. Fig. 33 shows the method of building up very wide doors known as *double margin* doors. The door actually consists of two narrow doors securely jointed at the meeting stiles. The two doors should be fitted separately. Then the rails are glued and wedged to the meeting stiles only. These stiles are then fixed together by three pairs of folding wedges, the ends of which are cleaned off at the bottom of the panel grooves. The mortises for the folding wedges are, of course, prepared at the same time as the other mortises in the stiles. The ends of the tenons should be kept short from the meeting edges; so that, when shrinkage takes place in the stiles, the joint will not be forced open. The joint may be rebated or it may be ploughed for a loose tongue, as shown by the alternative details in Fig. 34.

When the inner stiles have been securely fixed, the panels are placed in position and the outer stiles wedged on the rails in the usual way. A metal bar is usually let into a groove in the top edge of the door, and screwed securely. This prevents the two leaves of the door from pulling apart.

Gothic Doors. This term is applied to doors that are designed to conform to Gothic architecture. They are generally used in church work. The special feature is the pointed head. Fig. 35 shows a door of this character. It is a framed and ledged door, but braces may be added if required. The battens are usually vee-jointed and the framing is chamfered on the back. Another feature of this type of door is the ornamental hinges. They are made of wrought iron, and in many buildings they are very ornate and beautiful examples of smith's work.

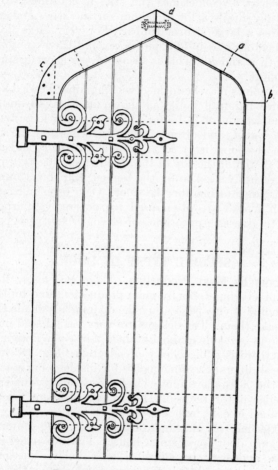

Fig. 35. Gothic or Tudor Door

The head of the door is usually in two pieces and jointed at *b*. Sometimes the stile is continued to *a*, but this entails a lot of labour on the stile, and also requires a large size of timber. For very large doors the head may be in four pieces, so that there are joints at both *a* and *b*. This is to avoid the short grain at the joints.

The joints may be formed with hammer-headed keys or with handrail bolts, as shown in Figs. 43 and 86 in the section on "Joints." Sometimes a loose tenon is used at *d*, and often a tenon is formed on the stile when the joint is at *b*. This is shown at *c*, and also by a sketch of the top of the stile in Fig. 36. Oak pins are generally used to fix the tenons, and sometimes as an ornamentation for the door. Oak pins and small coach screws are often used for decorative purposes and to give an appearance of strength to this type of door.

SPECIAL TYPES OF DOORS

Doors by Mass Production. There are many firms manufacturing doors by mass production, and builders often find it cheaper to buy the doors ready made than to make them. The designs are very varied, and many different sizes may be obtained for each design, so that there is a big choice of selection. Fig. 15 shows several different arrangements for inside doors stocked by the manufacturers. They are usually made of Douglas fir or redwood, but many of them may be obtained in oak, mahogany, and teak.

External, or Entrance Doors. Fig. 37 shows an entrance door for a small house. The top panel is of glass, and may be elliptical or circular. The panel containing the glass is the same thickness as the door framing, and it is moulded and rebated in the usual way. It is built up of four pieces mitred at the corners.

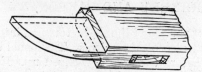

FIG. 36. DETAIL OF STILE

FIG. 37. EXTERNAL DOOR

The edges of the panel should be tongued into the door framing and also at the mitres. The panel should be completed before the door is wedged up. If the glass is of leaded lights the bars should be omitted. The

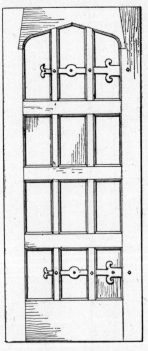

FIG. 38. ENTRANCE DOOR

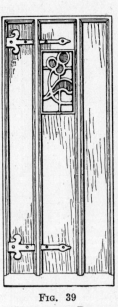

FIG. 39
LAMINWOOD DOOR

planted elliptical moulding round the glass panel, and the apron moulding help to cover the joints between the panel and the door framing.

The entrance door, shown in Fig. 38, is made of oak, and is intended to give an appearance of strength and solidity. The horizontal rails are bevelled on the top edge. The panels are of plywood, and may be in one piece across the door, or they may be jointed behind the vertical strips. The latter are planted on one or both sides of the door, making a twelve-panelled door. Wrought-iron sham hinges are used for ornamentation only, as the door is hung by ordinary butts.

Solid Doors. The improvements in plywood and laminated wood have allowed for the construction of doors without

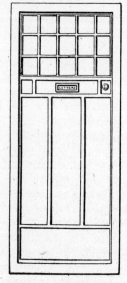

FIG. 40. METAL DOOR   FIG. 41. FLUSH DOOR

framing. Fig. 39 shows a door of this type. The panels are formed by planting moulded cover fillets

on one or both sides of the door. Leaded lights
and sham ornamental hinges are added to improve
the appearance. The weather-board is to throw the
water off the threshold and to give an appearance of
a bottom rail. Block-board is generally used for this
type of door.

Metal Doors. Fig. 40 shows a metal door with oak
plywood panels, kicking plate, and small lights. It
is supplied fitted with furniture. Further details of
this class of work will be given in the section on "Metal
Casements."

Flush Doors. This type of door has superseded the
panel door in nearly all types of buildings. The development has been rapid within recent years, and the better
qualities are fire, damp, and, in some cases, sound-
resisting. They have unbroken plane surfaces, except
for special cases where supervision is necessary, as in
hospitals, etc., when a small glass panel is introduced
at the top.

The various types are: (1) Framed, and faced with
plywood. (2) An outer frame with fibre core. (3) Laminwood. (4) Superior doors with veneered faces. There
is great variation in the construction and finishings,
and every firm has its own particular method. Origi-
nally the doors were subject to blistering, peeling, and
chipping of the ply edges, but they are now free from
these defects. The chief improvement is in the bonding
materials, or glues. Ordinary glue is not satisfactory,
and casein or film glues are used. The development of
synthetic resins as bonding materials is still affecting
the construction of flush doors, and new types are
continually being introduced. The processes demand
expensive equipment so that large scale manufacture
is necessary for economic production.

Framed Core. The usual type consists of a deal
framed core faced with plywood as shown in Fig. 41.

The top and bottom rails are tenoned into the stiles, but the intermediate rails have short stub tenons resting in a continuous groove in the stile. Some firms use butt joints for the rails and depend upon the bonding material providing the stability. Corrugated joint fasteners are used to give additional security. A lock block is provided on one or both edges according to the type of door.

Sometimes the rails are bored to allow for a free current of air through the door. This is to equalize the outer and inner pressures, temperatures, humidity, and change of moisture content. Usually, however, the ventilation is provided at the joint between rail and stile, as shown in Fig. 42.

Another type of door has a lattice of vertical ribs slotted in the top and bottom rails. This is for small doors, and short staggered rails are added for larger doors. For cabinet work and small doors generally, this type of construction has been superseded by blockboard. Fibre cores are used in many cases to make the door more insulating,

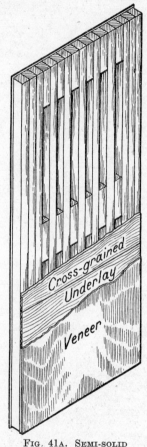

FIG. 41A. SEMI-SOLID
CONSTRUCTION

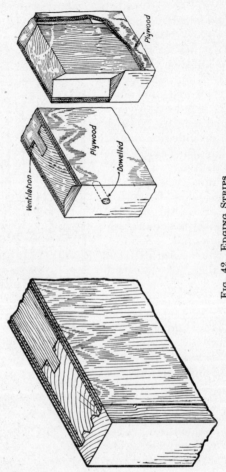

FIG. 42. EDGING STRIPS

and in special cases cork or asbestos is used for sound- or fire-resisting.

Semi-solid Doors. Fig. 41A shows a type known as semi-solid construction which is now very popular. There is much variation in the amount of wood used. It is usual to cover the core with an underlay, with the grain running horizontally, and then to veneer the surfaces.

Edging Strips. These form an important part in the manufacture of a good door. They are also called clashings, bandings, margins, and railings; but edgings is a more suitable and common term. Their function is to hide and secure the edges of the plywood and veneers, and to give a superior finish to that of the core. Fig. 42 shows several variations but there are many others. In cheap work they are only applied to the shutting stile, hence the name clashings. In superior doors, however, they are mitred round the top and both edges and sometimes dowelled, as shown.

Surface Finishings. The finished surface may show the grain of the wood. Even in cheap doors this is very effective, especially with rotary cut Douglas fir, which shows a bold handsome grain when stained and varnished. Plain plywoods are painted or cellulosed. For veneered and polished doors the decorative possibilities are unlimited with the many figured woods available. For special purposes metal-faced doors are made, and various metal finishes are obtainable as described in the section on "Timber."

HANGING DOORS

Fitting Doors. The door should be laid horizontally on two sawing stools, and the sizes of the opening transferred to the door. Two laths are convenient for this purpose. The surplus wood is sawn off, but it is necessary to test the opening to see if it is square before cutting the door to the correct sizes. If the door is too short it is best to plant a piece between the horns before they are sawn off. The top and bottom edges are difficult to plane, hence it is advisable to cut the door as near to the finished height as possible. The vertical edges are easy to plane, and the width of the door should be left full for fitting in the opening. The door is then tested in the opening, and $\frac{1}{16}$ in. allowed at the sides and top for clearance. The clearance at the bottom depends upon the floor coverings.

Hinging. Two 3-in. butt hinges are usually sufficient for the ordinary interior door. Hardwood doors in good-class work usually have three hinges. The hinges should be *let in* both door and frame. The door is placed on its edge and the position for the hinges is marked. The top hinge should be just below the top rail, and the bottom hinge just above the bottom rail when there are three hinges. When there are two hinges the positions are about 8 in. from the top, and 12 in. from the bottom for a 6 ft. 6 in. door.

A marking gauge is set to half the thickness of the hinge, less *half the clearance* of the joint. This gauge is used for gauging the depth for *letting in* the hinge both in the edge of the door and in the frame. The width of the hinge to be let into the door requires careful consideration. If the door-frame stile is not *plumb*, that is, if it is overhanging at the top, it is often necessary to put the top hinge further in than the bottom hinge. This lifts, or *cocks*, the nose of the door as it opens, and enables it to clear the floor. To judge the amount of eccentricity of the knuckles required, it is best to rear the door so that the edge of the door is against the hanging stile of the frame and with the door at right angles to the frame.

If the door is required to open flat to the wall and it has to clear an architrave, it is necessary to have

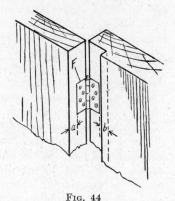

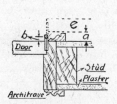

FIG. 43
HANGING DOORS

FIG. 44
HANGING DOOR

FIG. 45
BUTT HINGE

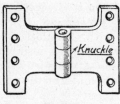

FIG. 46
PARLIAMENT HINGE

FIG. 47
RISING BUTT

the knuckles of the hinges projecting out from the face
of the door. This is illustrated in Fig. 43. In this case
it is required to give a clearance *a* when the door is
opened to the position *e*. Hence, the knuckle of the
hinge must have a projection *b* over the face of the
door, which is *half* of the distance *a*. Special hinges,
known as parliament hinges, see Fig. 46, may be
obtained for exceptional cases of this description.

Another marking gauge is set for gauging the edge
of the door stile for the flaps of the hinges. When the
hinges have been *let in* and screwed to the door, as
shown at *F*, Fig. 44, they are opened and the door is
placed in position in the rebates. The door is *packed
up* on chisels or wedges to the correct height, and the
position of the hinges is marked on the edge of the
lining. The door is removed and the marks squared
on to the rebate.

When *letting in* the flap in the rebate it is better to
mark the position *b* from the *stop* rather than to gauge
it from the edge of the lining. That is, *b* should be a
little more than *a*, Fig. 44, sufficient to allow for six
coats of paint. This is often overlooked when hanging doors, so that when the door and linings are
painted the door *binds* and removes the paint on the
door.

The lining is next cut to receive the flaps of the
hinges in the same way as for the door. When the door
is ready for screwing in position it is placed at right
angles to the linings and *packed up* on wedges,
so that the hinges coincide with the sinkings on the
lining ; and one screw to each hinge is inserted. The
door is tested to see if it closes satisfactorily, and any
necessary adjustments are made, and then the remainder
of the screws are inserted.

The flaps should be sunk into the door and frame,
as shown at *F*, Fig. 44, so that they are flush, and the

screw heads must not project above the faces of the flaps. These precautions ensure that the hinges will not bind when the door is closed.

DOOR FURNITURE

Hinges. There are many other forms of hinges in addition to those already shown for batten doors. The most common type is the butt hinge, Fig. 45, which may be of cast iron, pressed steel, or brass. Butt hinges may be obtained in a large number of sizes. The pin is made of steel in most hinges, no

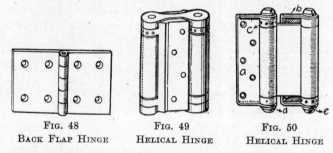

FIG. 48
BACK FLAP HINGE

FIG. 49
HELICAL HINGE

FIG. 50
HELICAL HINGE

matter what the metal of the hinge may be. Butt hinges are generally used where the edge of the door is sufficiently thick to receive them.

Parliament Hinges, Fig. 46, are used where it is required to open the door flat to the wall on which there are projecting mouldings, etc. Another variety of the parliament hinge is the egg-shaped, or pew, hinge. It is used for ornamental purposes, and usually on pew doors. The knuckle is specially shaped in the form of an egg, hence its name.

The Rising Butt, Fig. 47, is used to lift the door as it opens, so that it may clear an uneven floor or a floor covering. They are similar to ordinary butts when the flaps are closed, and they are fixed to the door and frame in the same way. The knuckle has a helical joint which raises one flap as it opens.

Pin Hinges are used where it is required to remove the door occasionally. They are ordinary butt hinges with a loose pin. The head of the pin is ornamented so that it may be removed easily, and it has a small flange to rest on the flaps.

Back Flaps. When the framing is too thin to receive butt hinges, it is usual to use back flap hinges, Fig. 48.

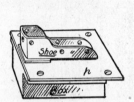

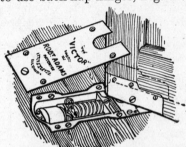

FIG. 51. FLOOR SPRING   FIG. 52. FLOOR SPRING

These are similar to butt hinges except that the flaps are larger. They are screwed on to the face of the framing instead of on the edges. Generally they are made of pressed steel or brass. When made of brass the flaps are very often ornamented.

Helical Hinges. Swing doors which open both ways require a special form of hinge. The cheapest form of hinge for this purpose is the helical hinge, Fig. 49, which shows the hinge closed. This is the condition of the hinge when it is fixed to the door and the door is closed. Fig. 50 shows the hinge with the springs released and one flap opened ready for fixing to the door. One flap *a* is fixed to the door and the other flap *b* to the frame. The barrels *d* and *e* contain springs which are tightened when the hinge is fixed in position.

A steel pin is inserted in the holes in the collar *c* for regulating the springs. When the door is swinging it rotates on each barrel in turn. These instructions only apply to the top hinge, which, of course, is in tension due to the weight of the door. The bottom hinge is a *blank*, and has no springs ; it is similar in design, however, for appearance.

Floor Springs. The helical hinge is not satisfactory for heavy doors, and floor springs are generally used. Fig. 51 shows the usual type. The shoe is fitted and screwed to the heel of the door. A square hole in the bottom of the shoe fits on to a pivot which is actuated by a spring in the box. A plate *p* can be removed for examining the spring when necessary ; but a screw (under the shoe) is provided for adjusting the closing speed. The box is let into the floor so that the plate *p* is flush with the floor. Fig. 52 shows a spring fixed in position with the door open. The plate has been removed to show the spring.

Floor springs may be obtained for rebated frames, and are used for silent closing. They are very similar to those for double-swing doors, and they are fixed in the same way. Usually, however, " door closers " are preferred. These are fixed to the head of the door and control the closing of the door. The door is hung with ordinary butt hinges.

LOCKS AND " FURNITURE "

Hand. There is considerable confusion in the meaning of the terms *left* and *right* hand when referring to doors and furniture. When the door is viewed from the side showing the knuckles of the hinges it is termed *left-* or *right-hand hung* according to the position of the hinges. It is a little more complicated, however, when dealing with the locks and furniture. The manufacturers name them as shown in Fig. 52A. If the door opens away

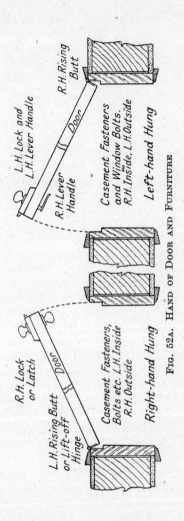

L.H. Lock and
L.H. Lever Handle

R.H. Rising
Butt

Door

R.H. Lever
Handle

Casement Fasteners
and Window Bolts.
R.H. Inside, L.H. Outside

Left-hand Hung

R.H. Lock
or Latch

Door

L.H. Rising Butt
or Lift-off
Hinge

Casement Fasteners,
Bolts etc. L.H. Inside
R.H. Outside

Right-hand Hung

Fig. 52A. Hand of Door and Furniture

from the operator with the lock on the right and the
bevel of the latch bolt facing the operator, it is termed
right-hand; otherwise it is left-hand. The illustration
also shows the distinctions for casement fastenings.

There are many different forms of locks. When a lock
is operated by a key only it is called a *dead lock*, and
when by a spindle only it is called a *latch*.

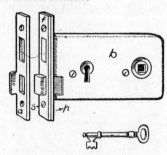

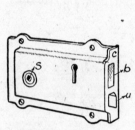

FIG. 53. RIM LOCK   FIG. 54. MORTISE LOCK

The Rim Lock, Fig. 53, serves as a latch and a lock.
A square spindle in the bush *s* operates the latch *a*
and a key *shoots* the bolt *b*. The spindle is controlled
by a pair of *knobs*, as shown in Fig. 56. These knobs,
or handles, are usually called the lock furniture, which
also includes *keyhole escutcheons* to cover the keyholes.
Roses are screwed to the door to cover the spindle
holes, and to steady the spindle. A *receiver*, or box,
is fixed to the door frame to receive the latch and bolt.
Only one rose and one escutcheon are required for a
rim lock, but two of each are required for a mortise
lock.

Mortise Locks. This type of lock is generally used
for inside doors. The chief advantage is that it is
buried in the stile of the door, hence it is not seen, and
cannot be removed when the door is closed. The
fixing of the lock entails a lot of labour, unless the

mortise for the lock is prepared when the door is made. The usual type serves as both a lock and a latch.

The latch is usually operated by a spindle like the rim lock, but there are several patent variations. The latest development is a vertical push button incorporated in the door pull. Another variation is operated like a Suffolk latch.

Fixing Mortise Lock. The lock should be laid on the face of the door in the required position, so that

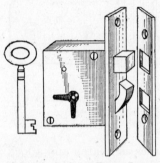

FIG. 56. LOCK FURNITURE

FIG. 55. SLIDING DOOR LOCK

the face plate *f* is flush with the edge of the door. The spindle and key holes are marked, and the positions of the face plate and body, or *case b*, are squared across the door edge. The key and spindle holes are bored; and also a series of holes is bored in the edge of the door, a little deeper than the length of the lock. The brace bit should be a little larger than the thickness of the case. A mortise-lock chisel is used to remove the waste wood. The lock is placed in the mortise and tested for the positions of the key and spindle holes. The face plate is then carefully marked and fitted into the door edge. When the lock is ready for screwing in position, the face plate is removed and the back-plate *p* is screwed to the door. The face plate is

secured to the back plate, which is part of the case, by
two small set-screws *s*. The striking plate *a* is let into
the rebate of the frame to receive the bolt and latch.

Barrel Mortise Locks may be obtained. They have
cylindrical cases which fit into one brace-bit hole. They

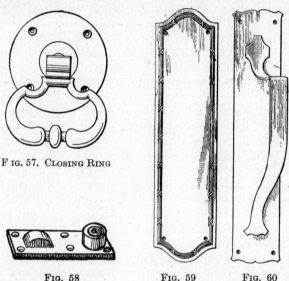

FIG. 57. CLOSING RING

FIG. 58
HOLDER AND STOP

FIG. 59
FINGER PLATE

FIG. 60
DOOR HANDLE

do not disturb the tenons, which is a fault of the ordinary
lock unless the lock rail has double tenons.

The Latch Lock, or night latch, is used for entrance
doors. The latch is operated by a key from the outside
and by a small knob on the inside. A small slide on
the inside fixes the latch in position so that the key
will not move the latch.

The Yale Lock is another type of lock used for
entrance doors. It has a neat appearance, and the
key is very small. The sides of the key are corrugated,

and the edge is shaped to operate a series of pins in the barrel of the lock. Both of these features make it difficult to duplicate the key except by a special machine. The key is numbered, however, for duplicating by the makers, if necessary. The case, on the inside of the door, is similar to a night latch, but smaller, and the latch is operated in the same way.

Sliding Doors require a special type of lock, as shown in Fig. 55. When the lock is fixed on the vertical edge of the door, and the door slides horizontally, the bolt is curved so that it shoots upwards *behind* the striking plate.

" **Lock Furniture** " may be of wood, glass, metal, or bakelite, and of varied design. Good furniture adds considerably to the appearance of a door. Metal sets may be finished brass, bronze, oxidized copper, oxidized silver, or nickel plated. Fig. 56 shows a plain pair of glass door knobs, and Fig. 57 shows a drop-ring in metal. The latter may be used for operating a latch, or simply for closing the door. Another different type is in the form of a lever.

Finger Plates, Fig. 59, are used to protect the paint and for ornamentation. They are placed above the lock on each side of the door ; sometimes they are also placed below the lock.

Door Handles, or door pulls, Fig. 60, are used on swing doors. They vary in length and in design considerably, and they are generally used as an ornamentation to the door.

Door Stops, Fig. 58, are used to prevent the door banging against the wall. The stop, which is made of rubber, is screwed to the floor at a convenient distance from the wall. Fig. 58 also shows a holder for keeping the door open. The holder is controlled by a spring and sinks below the surface of the plate by a downward pressure.

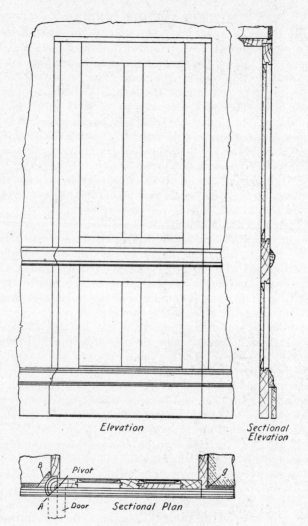

Elevation

Sectional
Elevation

Sectional Plan

FIG. 61. JIB DOOR

MISCELLANEOUS DOORS

Jib Doors, Fig. 61, are doors that are disguised as far as possible so that they present an unbroken surface with the wall. The importance of the details depends upon the secrecy required for the door. The panels are flush with the door framing on the face, but the back of the door is moulded in the usual way. The skirting, dado, moulding, etc., have an unbroken appearance. When the walls are painted it is usual to glue canvas over the door so that the joints of the door framing are not seen. It is better to omit the grounds and to plaster up to the framing, as shown at *g*. Another aid to the disguising of the door is to run a plate shelf round the room just above the top rail of the door.

Preparing the Mouldings. The difficulty of this door lies in the projecting mouldings on the face of the door. The door is hung on pivots at the top and bottom. The method of finding the cuts at *A* is to draw a 45° line from the centre of the pivot to the face of the skirting. The various members of the mouldings must be drawn in the plan of the skirting. A point on each member is obtained where it is cut by the 45° line. From these points describe circular arcs from the pivot centre, as shown. The circular arcs are the paths of the various members of the mouldings ; and the cuts for the joint must follow the arcs, or the tangents to the arcs. Hence, it will be seen that it is necessary to *cove out* for the path of the moving skirting and the dado rail, which are attached to the door.

If the wall is studded the *coving out* is simplified considerably, but in a brick wall it is usual to fix blocks *B* to receive the covings. The blocks make the recesses more dustproof. The details at *A* and *B* only apply to where the mouldings are recessed into the wall ; the remainder of the lining is the same as on the shutting side.

The shutting joint will be square to the face unless the door is narrow, or the base projects considerably over the face of the door. In these cases the shutting joint must be bevelled, as explained in the section on " Joints."

Dwarf Doors are doors less than 5 ft. in height. They provide difficulties only when they are surmounted by a capping and have projecting mouldings on the face. The construction for the capping was explained in the section on " Joints " ; and the method of preparing the projecting mouldings is the same as for the jib doors.

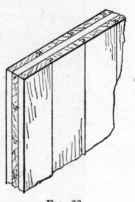

FIG. 62
FIRE-RESISTING DOOR

Warehouse Doors are large framed, ledged and braced doors filled in with battens in the usual way. These doors usually run on pulleys either on the ground or overhead ; hence the braces are placed diagonally in both directions because they have to keep the door rigid and square. There is a large variety of registered fittings on the market for *hanging* doors of this description. The same type of door is often used for yard gates to large works but with more precautions against the weather.

Wicket Gates are small doors arranged in larger doors, so that individuals may pass through without moving the larger door. They are usually about 4 ft. 6 in. high by 2 ft. wide. When they are placed in warehouse doors and large gates that are formed of battens, they should have the boards of the wicket gate in line with those of the larger gate ; this involves a little extra labour, but if the battens are uneven the door looks unsightly.

Revolving Shutters have superseded large doors of the warehouse type within recent years. They are less

(*Elliott's, Reading*)

FIG. 63. REVOLVING DOORS

cumbersome and easier to handle ; and they may be raised a small amount, whereas the door exposes the whole of the opening. The latter feature is important in inclement weather for warehouses and workshops.

Garage Doors. These may be framed and ledged,

but there are numerous types of revolving shutters specially designed for garages. Another kind consists

(*Elliott's, Reading*)

FIG. 63A. REVOLVING DOORS IN USE AS DOUBLE-SWING DOORS

of narrow doors that run round against the side walls on rails, or they may be folded like a partition.

Stable Doors are framed, ledged, and braced doors made in two halves. The bottom half is bolted on the

inside near the top, and the top half is usually fitted
with a stock lock, or padlock.

Fireproof Doors. It is important that communicating
doors between adjacent rooms in mills should be
fireproof. This type of door is usually of iron, and is
arranged to close auto-
matically by pulleys
running on an inclined
rail. An alternative

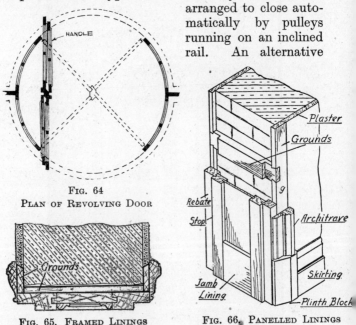

FIG. 64
PLAN OF REVOLVING DOOR

FIG. 65. FRAMED LININGS

FIG. 66. PANELLED LININGS

very often adopted is to build up a solid door of three
layers of tongued and grooved boards, as shown in Fig.
62, and then to cover the whole with tin-plate.

Teak is the most fireproof of timbers, but any
timber may be chemically treated to make it more
non-combustible. Solidity is also a good security
against fire, and it is for this reason that the doors
are built up as in Fig. 62. There are numerous

registered types of fire-resisting doors, but they are made by specialist firms.

Revolving Doors. These doors are generally used for the entrances to public buildings. They usually consist of four wings revolving round a central axis in the form of a turnstile. The chief advantage is that they are draught-proof. They may be obtained with either two or four compartments. The wings may be collapsed either to the centre or to one side when required, to give an uninterrupted passage.

A general view of a " four-compartment " revolving door is shown in Fig. 63 and 63A ; and a plan, showing the wings collapsed to the side, is shown in Fig. 64.

DOOR FINISHINGS

Door Linings. The frames for internal doors are called *casings*, or *linings*. The simplest form is shown in Fig. 43. The width of the linings varies with the type of wall. In this example a studded wall is shown, but the same type of lining would be used for $4\frac{1}{2}$ in. brickwork or breeze blocks. For inferior work the rebate is often formed by planting a $1\frac{1}{2}$ in. by $\frac{1}{2}$ in. piece, whilst the lining itself is only 1 in. thick. The linings must be sufficiently thick to give a secure hold to the screws for the hinges. Some-times blocks are fixed to the back of the lining to give more screw-hold.

Framed Linings. For walls over 9 in. thick it is necessary to frame the linings as shown in Figs. 65 and 66, or to build them up as shown at *a* in Fig. 67. This allows for much variation in treat-ment according to the quality of

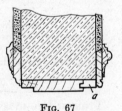

FIG. 67
MOULDED GROUNDS

the work. The usual method for good work is shown in Fig. 66, which is for a $1\frac{1}{2}$ brick wall.

The Grounds, *g*, Fig. 66, are first fixed to the brick-work by means of plugs, pallets, or breeze blocks, and the level grounds are dovetailed into them.   They are usually left " off the saw," and bevelled to form a key for the plaster.   They are fixed before the plastering is done, and serve as a guide to the plasterer.

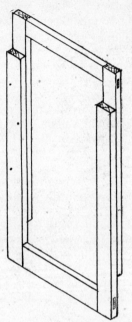
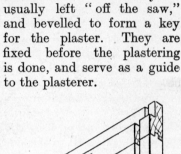
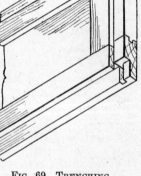

FIG. 68. WEDGING-UP
FRAMED GROUNDS

FIG. 69. TRENCHING
SOFFIT LINING

Moulded Grounds, Fig. 67, are sometimes used to form a bolder architrave ; in this case the grounds are machine planed, and cleaned up on the edge.

Framed Grounds. For first-class work in hardwood the grounds are often framed together before fixing. The angles are mortised and tenoned.   They are wedged together in pairs, by lightly nailing the vertical grounds together face to face with the heads at opposite ends,

as shown in Fig. 68. They are conveyed to the job
in this condition.

Panelled Linings. Fig. 66 is an isometric view showing the various details for good-class panelled linings.
The rebates, or door frames, are framed together
separately and tongued into
the *stop*. This arrangement
allows for shrinkage without
disturbing any of the joints.
The soffit, or head, lining, is
panelled in the same way as
the jamb linings.   The panels
are usually moulded to match
the doors. Fig. 65 shows an
example in which the panelled

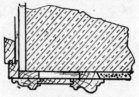

Fig. 70. Framed
Architrave

framing is rebated to receive the door. This method
is not so good, but it is usually adopted for ordinary
work.

The Soffit is trenched to receive the jamb linings.

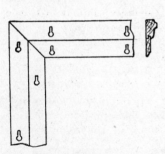

Fig. 71. Fixing by
Slot-screws

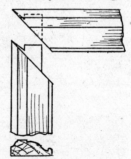

Fig. 72. Tenoned
Architrave

A tongue is formed on the top of the jamb linings,
on the face of the lining usually, to engage with the
trench in the soffit.   The method is shown in Fig. 69.
Sometimes the trench is omitted in the rebate, especially

if the door is less than 2 in. thick. In some cases the trench in the rebate is stopped $\frac{1}{2}$ in. from the outside edge so that it is not seen on the face. When the architrave covers the edge, however, this is an unnecessary precaution.

Architraves. The architraves break the joint between the plaster and grounds, and provide ornamentation.

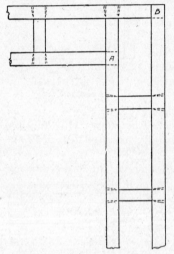

FIG. 73. SKELETON GROUNDS FOR FRAMED ARCHITRAVE

They may be single, as in Figs. 65 and 67, or double, as in Fig. 66, or they may be framed as in Fig. 70. The architrave is usually in one piece if it is less than 5 in. wide. When it is more than 5 in. wide it should be in two pieces, otherwise the shrinkage will break the mitres.

The architraves are usually nailed to the grounds and to the edge of the linings. In the best work, however, they are often fixed by slot screws, especially if they are of polished hardwood. The screws are fixed in the grounds and left projecting about $\frac{5}{16}$ in., and then the back of the architrave is prepared, as shown in Fig. 71.

Tenoned Architraves. When architraves are fixed by slot screws it is usual to fix the mitres by mortise and tenon, feathers, or hardwood keys. Fig. 72 shows the mitre prepared as a mortise and tenon joint. When it is prepared it is glued and screwed from the back.

The set of architraves is placed on to the screws

and tapped down from the top. It requires two men for the work, one driving the architrave down and the other tapping it on the face over the screws to keep it tight to the linings and grounds.

Framed Architraves. Very wide architraves are sometimes framed, as shown in Fig. 70. This type of architrave requires a special kind of ground, known as *skeleton ground*. The usual arrangement is

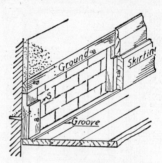

FIG. 74. PLINTH BLOCK

FIG. 75. FIXING SKIRTING BOARDS

shown in Fig. 73. For convenience of assembling the joint at *B* is an open mortise or a halved joint, whilst that at *A* is a halved joint.

Plinth Blocks are used to give a bolder appearance to the foot of the architrave and to provide an abutting surface for the end of the skirting. They are usually fixed to the architrave by a dovetailed feather. Fig. 74 shows the back of the block prepared for the feather, which is glued and screwed to the block.

Skirting Boards. For inferior work the skirtings are scribed to the floor, as previously explained, and nailed to plugs. This method is objectionable, because the shrinking of the skirting and the joists leaves a space between the skirting and the floor, after a time. The

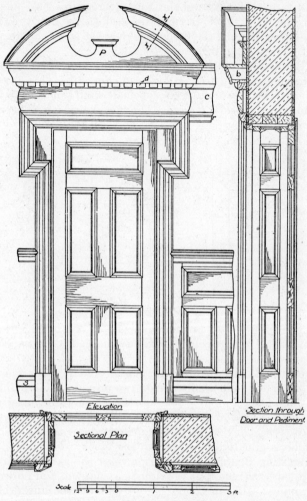

Elevation

Sectional Plan

Section through
Door and Pediment.

Scale

Fɪɢ. 76. Iɴsɪᴅᴇ Dᴏᴏʀ ᴀɴᴅ Fɪɴɪsʜɪɴɢs

defect is often overcome by nailing a fillet in the form of a quarter circle to the floor, but it is unsightly.

For superior work of the type shown in Fig. 66, it is usual to fix grounds as shown in Fig. 75. The horizontal ground is placed just below the top edge of the skirting. The vertical grounds, or *soldiers s*, are placed about every three bricks apart. The space between the grounds should be plastered flush. The example shows the skirting built up of two pieces. The bottom edge is tongued into a groove running round the floor. The groove assists in secret-fixing the bottom edge of the skirting, which only requires nailing at the top edge, behind the groove for the top part of the skirting. A very wide base should be fixed by slot screws, was shown in the illustration. The top moulding of the skirting is fixed in a groove in the base and by slot screws near the top edge.

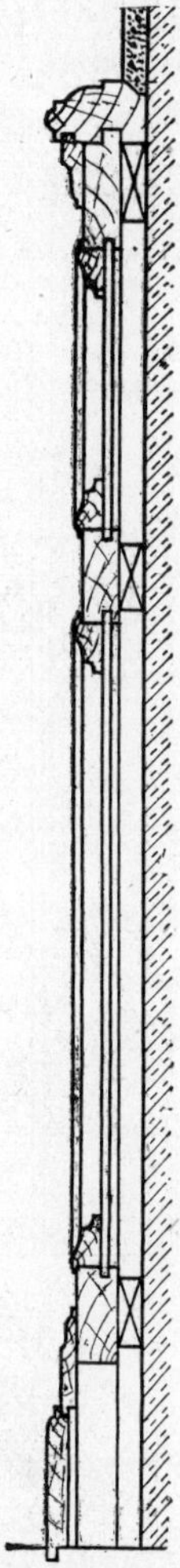

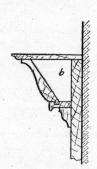

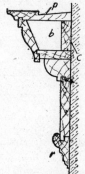

FIG. 77. SEC-
TION THROUGH
DADO

FIG. 78
SECTION THROUGH
PEDIMENT

FIG. 79
SECTION THROUGH
CORNICE

Superior Inside Door. A door with finishings suitable for a dining room is shown in Fig. 76. Alternative

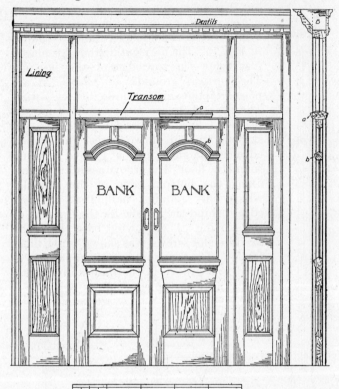

FIG. 80. VESTIBULE DOORS AND FRAME

methods of finishing the dado are shown. The panelled dado, which is shown by a vertical section in Fig. 77, would be fixed to grounds as previously explained. The other side has a plaster finish with a skirting and dado rail. It is usual to fix ornamental paper, such as lincrusta, or apply plastic paint between the skirting and the dado rail.

The Pediment, or overdoor *P*, is often used for good-class work, especially for vestibule doors to public buildings. A section on *x-x* is shown in Fig. 78. This shows the method of building up the moulding.

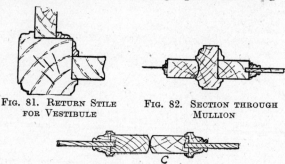

FIG. 81. RETURN STILE   FIG. 82. SECTION THROUGH
     FOR VESTIBULE   MULLION

FIG. 83. SECTION THROUGH DOOR STILES

The Cornice *C* may be carried round the room in the form of a plate shelf *p* and picture rail *r*, as shown in Fig. 79. The dentils *d* may be omitted, but in any case they would only be placed over the door. The projecting mouldings for the plate shelf should be supported by blocks *b*, placed about 2 ft. 6 in. apart round the room ; or a continuous ground *c* could be used as a substitute for the blocks if the amount of projection over the face of the wall were small.

Vestibule Frames. Fig. 80 shows the elevation and vertical section of the doors and frame for a vestibule suitable for a bank or other public building. The construction for this type of frame is very similar in all cases, but the ornamentation varies considerably. The example shows the frame fixed between two walls, but very often the panelling is returned at right angles to form a vestibule from the main office. In this case a return stile is used, as shown in Fig. 81, which also shows the method of fixing the panelling in the framing.

A section through the mullion is shown in Fig. 82, and a section through the meeting stiles of the swing doors is shown in Fig. 83. The mouldings *a* and *b*, Fig.

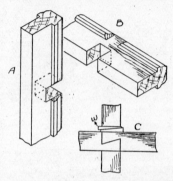

Fig. 84. Details for Vestibule Framing

80, are usually planted, but they may be stuck on the solid. The cornice at the ceiling should follow the design of the plaster cornice as far as possible ; alternative details are shown. Blocks *B* are used to carry the mouldings.

The top panels of the frame and of the door are of glass, which is usually embossed or painted with gilt lettering. The top panels of the wings and of the return panelling may be of ornamental glass or of wood, as shown in the illustration.

Alternative details for the joint between the transom and the mullion are shown in Fig. 84. The joint shown at *A* and *B* is a halving joint with mitred moulding. This is the easiest form of construction, and allows for a continuous transom. The alternative method is a mortise and tenon joint with dovetailed tenons. This

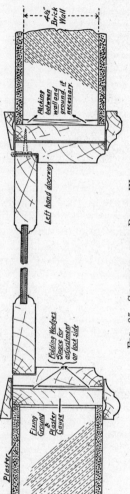

4½ Brick Wall

Packing between wall and ground if necessary.

Left hand doorway

Folding Wedges Space for adjustment on lock side

Fixing Ground & Plaster Gauge

Plaster

FIG. 85. SECTIONS FOR BRICK WALLS

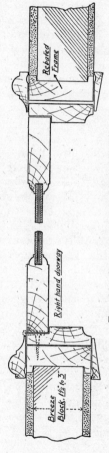

Rebated Frame

Right hand doorway

Breeze Block 1½ to 3"

FIG. 86. SECTIONS FOR BLOCK PARTITION

is shown by a vertical section through the centre at C. The dovetailed tenons are secured by two folding wedges which are trimmed off level with the rebates.

"**Evos**" **Doors.** This is a doorway assembly in which everything is prepared before sending to the job. The architraves are mitred and cut to size ready for fixing to the framing; the door is fitted and hung, and the lock escutcheons and striking plate are fixed. By mass production and standardization of sizes the Evos Doorways Ltd., Grosvenor Gardens, S.W.1, claim a saving of 35 per cent in costs in the completed doorway.

Grounds are first fixed square, plumb, and out of winding in the opening, as shown in Figs. 85 and 86. For thin walls, such as breeze blocks and metal lathing, it is necessary to run the grounds to the ceiling joists for secure fixing. The grounds are hollowed out for fixing the breeze blocks, as shown in Fig. 86. For brick walls the grounds are plain and fixed in the usual way.

Fixing the Doorway. The door is unlocked and opened, and the hanging jamb is fixed to the ground through the rebate. Two screws, one through each butt, assist in the fixing. The jamb on the lock side is first packed by small wedges, if necessary, before securing to the ground.

The Architraves may be obtained plain or moulded. They are grooved on the back to allow for any projection where the plaster meets the grounds. This ensures a tight fit on the lining on the inside edge and on the plaster at the outside edge. They are prepared ready for fixing in position.

The Hinges, lock, and furniture are fixed before leaving the works; hence, the doorway is completed when it is fixed to the grounds and the architraves nailed in position. The appearance of the completed doorway is the same as that fixed in the ordinary way.

PANELLING

Panelling is the term generally applied to fixed panel framing. The construction entails no details other than those used in the construction of doors. When the panelling is not fixed on to a wall it is called

FIG. 87. WALL PANELLING

a screen or a partition. Wall panelling is only finished on the face side. The back is left " off the saw " or machine planed. The panels are mulleted on the circular saw without thicknessing them, unless they are of plywood.

The height of wall panelling varies considerably. Usually it is only of dado height, but often it is carried to the same height as the door shown in Fig. 87. Occasionally the whole of the walls of a room are covered with panelling, but not so often as formerly.

Dado framing is shown in Fig. 76. The stiles usually run through and the rails are tenoned into them. Exceptions will be shown in " Church Work." The muntins are stub-tenoned between the rails, and may be screwed from the back. The panels are usually moulded with panel moulding. If the moulding is stuck on the solid the angles may be mitred, scribed, or finished with mason's stops. Stop cham-

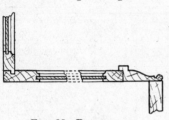

FIG. 88. DETAILS FOR DADO FRAMING

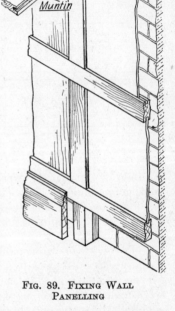

FIG. 89. FIXING WALL PANELLING

fers are often used in place of mouldings.

The panelling is fixed to grounds, as shown in Fig. 77, by nailing, screwing, or by slot-screws. The archi-trave is often rebated on the back to receive the stile of the framing, and the internal angles are usually tongued.

Both of these details are shown in Fig. 88. External angles are usually mitred.

Built-up Panelling. The framing is usually finished in the shop ready for erection. Fig. 89 shows Elliott's method of building up the panelling in position. The various members are

prepared ready for fixing, and vertical grounds are
fixed to the wall in the usual way. The rails are fixed

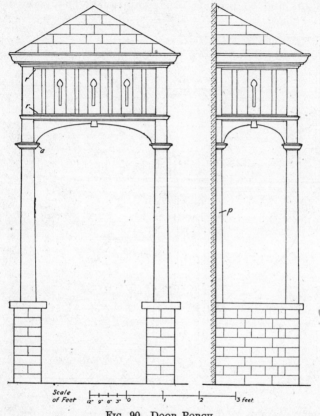

FIG. 90. DOOR PORCH

to the grounds by metal buttons, and the muntins have
a pair of tenons and are slotted, so as to clear the
button when they are in position. The remainder of the
details are similar to those in other types of framing.

PORCHES AND DOOR-HOODS

Porches and hoods are used to protect entrance doors and to provide ornamentation. They may be

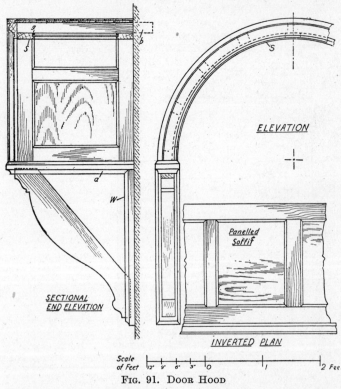

ELEVATION

Panelled Soffit

SECTIONAL END ELEVATION

INVERTED PLAN

Scale of Feet   12" 9" 6" 3" 0   1   2 Fee

FIG. 91. DOOR HOOD

very varied in design, and porches may be open or closed.

Porch. An example of a porch suitable for a small entrance door is shown in Fig. 90. The brickwork may be dispensed with, and the posts carried down to the step. The sides are often filled in with glazed sashes

for greater protection against the weather. It is better
to let the neck moulds *a* into the post for about ¼ in.
than to plant them on the face ; this protects the
moulding against the weather, and gives greater
security for the fixing. The rails *r* are tenoned between
the posts that run up to carry the fascia. The fascia
carries the gutter, which is the ordinary type of C.I.
gutter fixed by galvanized screws. It is usual to make
the posts *p* half the thickness of the outer posts, and
to plug them to the wall.

The same design may be adopted for two adjacent
doors in terrace or semi-detached houses. The feet
of the outer posts should be dowelled to the stone
coping. Lead or concrete flats, above the porch, are
often used, especially where slating or tiling interferes
with an upstairs window, or where economy is an
important consideration.

Hoods are similar to porches in many respects, but
they are supported by brackets fixed to the wall instead
of being carried to the ground. Flat hoods
are often suspended from above, or canti-
levered ; but usually brackets are used,
similar to the one shown in Fig. 91. The
example shows a hood for a door with a
semicircular fanlight. The panelled soffit
s will have the curved pieces cut from the
solid, and made continuous by a halving
joint securely screwed. Plywood is the
best material for the panels. It is bent
into the rebates on the back of the framing, and held in position by small beads

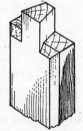

Fig. 92
Dovetail for
Bracket

g, like glass beads, as shown in the vertical section.

The bearers *b* rest on the panelled soffit and are
wedged into the brickwork. Thin boards, in two
thicknesses, are bent round the bearers, and securely
fixed to the bracket and the bottom bearers to prevent

the ends from springing away. The top of the hood
is covered with sheet lead.

The Brackets supporting the hood could be used for
carrying a flat or a gabled hood. The wall piece *w* is

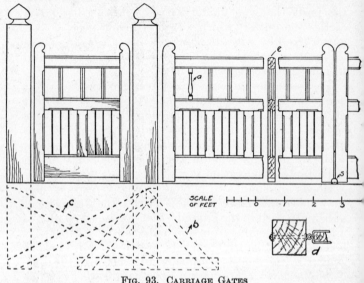

FIG. 93. CARRIAGE GATES

plugged to the brickwork and is fixed to the piece *a*
by a single dovetail, as shown in Fig. 92. The construction of this joint is important, as it must be made
to prevent the piece *a* pulling away from piece *w*. This
form of bracket is often called a *gallows bracket* because
it is capable of carrying a suspended weight at the end.

GATES

There is much variation in the design of gates, according to the position and the security and amount of
ornamentation required. The most common type is

framed, ledged, and braced, as explained for warehouse doors. They may be filled in with close boarding, or battens, or they may be *lagged*. Lags are usually about 3 in. wide, and they are spaced about 2 in. apart. An example is shown in Fig. 94.

Carriage Gates. An example of a pair of large gates for a carriage drive is shown in Fig. 93. Ornamentation

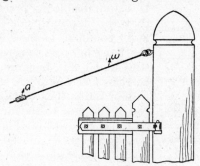

FIG. 94. HANGING WIDE GATES

is usually the chief consideration. They are usually accompanied by a small side gate for foot traffic. The lower part of the gate shown in the example is panelled with tongued and grooved boarding, and the framing is stop-chamfered. The upper part may have ornamental wrought iron panels, or bars, as shown in Fig. 93. The bars may be square in section and placed diagonally, or they may be turned bars, as shown at *a*. A very effective method is to have the bars square-turned. A vertical section at *e* shows the method of weathering the rails.

Hanging the Gates. Bands and gudgeons are used for hanging gates. The straps of the hinges should be on both sides of the gate, as shown at *d*, Fig. 93, so that the bolts pass through the gate and both straps.

The Gudgeons are usually in the form of bolts when

the posts are of wood, and they pass through the post
as shown at *d*. When the posts are of stone the gudgeon
is made ragged and leaded into a dovetailed hole. For
brick pillars they should be built in the courses with
anchors, or bolted as for timber posts.

Wide Gates for level crossings, works, etc., are hung
in the same way, but it is necessary to support the nose.

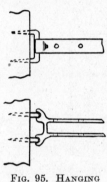

FIG. 95. HANGING
GATES

It is impossible to brace them so
that the nose will not drop. The
most common method is to carry
the hanging post, or the hanging
stile, about 3 ft. or more above the
height of the gate. A strong steel
wire or rod is then carried from the
top of the post to the far end of the
gate, as shown in Fig. 94. A
tension sleeve *a*, in the form of a
bolt with right- and left-hand
threads, can be adjusted so that the
wire or rod can be kept to the
required length for keeping the nose
clear of the ground.

Another method is to have a roller under the nose
and a narrow wrought-iron plate in the shape of a
quadrant fixed on the surface of the ground. The roller
runs along the plate and prevents the nose from
dropping.

Rising Hinges. When the ground is uneven it is
necessary to *cock* the gudgeons as previously explained
for hinging doors. Field gates, or gates that open in
either direction, require special gudgeons. Fig. 95 shows
the plan and elevation of a strap hinge to enable a
gate to clear rising ground in both directions. The band
is specially made to fit on to two strong *dogs*, which
are driven into the posts. The top band and gudgeon
are of the ordinary type.

Stops. For single gates it is usual to screw a wrought-iron stop, in the form of a bracket, to the post. Double gates require a stop on the ground at the centre, as shown at *s* in Fig. 93. In this case the stop is hinged so that it can be dropped level with the ground when the gates are opened.

Fixing the Posts. It is necessary that the posts be fixed securely. The gates will soon pull the posts out of the vertical if they are insecure. One method is to bed them in concrete. Sometimes long bolts are used to tighten the posts on to wooden distance pieces. Another method is to brace the posts by bolting strong diagonal pieces to the posts, as shown at *C*, Fig. 93. Any method which connects the two posts necessitates the digging of a trench in the ground for the full width of the gateway. This is sometimes objected to, and the posts have to be fixed independently. If concrete is not used it is necessary to strut the posts, as shown at *b*, Fig. 93. Sole plates should be placed at right angles to each other, and the struts *b* should be placed on all four sides. If the method *C* is used, or bolts and distance pieces, it is necessary to strut the posts in the other direction. All the timber below the surface of the ground should be creosoted, or treated in some other way, to prevent decay.

SECTION VI

GEOMETRY

BY

J. F. DOWSETT, A.I.Struct.E.

SECTION VI

GEOMETRY

PLANE GEOMETRY

A GEOMETRICAL *point* is said to have position but no magnitude. In graphical work, however, a point must have magnitude to enable it to be seen. For accurate graphical work a finely-pointed needle is the best instrument for marking points, since it permits the draughtsman to make points of the smallest size.

A *Line* may be said to be the path (or locus) of a moving point, and may be defined as having length but no breadth or thickness. There, again, theoretical perfection may not be attained in graphical work, but lines conforming as nearly as possible to the state implied by the definition should be used in geometrical constructions.

A *Straight Line* may be defined in the following ways, each definition indicating an important property of the line : (1) The shortest distance between two given points ; (2) the locus of a point moving with unchanging direction ; (3) a line such that when revolved about any definite part of its length as a fixed axis, all points in the line retain fixed positions.

A *Curve* may be defined as the locus of a point moving with constantly changing direction.

A *Plane* may be defined as a surface such that if a straight line be drawn through any two points in the surface the line will lie wholly in the surface.

A *Horizontal Plane* may be considered as a plane parallel to the surface of still water.

A *Vertical Plane* is any plane perpendicular to a horizontal plane.

The term *Parallel* is used to indicate a constant mean distance between two or more lines, two or more surfaces, or between lines and surfaces.

The term *Perpendicular* is used to indicate that the angle between two straight lines, or two planes, or between a straight line and a plane, is a right angle, i.e. 90°.

The measure of an angle is the measure of the difference in the directions of two straight lines.

Complementary Angles are any two angles which are together equal to 90° (one right angle).

Supplementary Angles are any two angles which are together equal to 180° (two right angles).

ANGULAR MEASURE AND USE OF SET-SQUARES

The student is assumed to be familiar with the units of " length," " area," and " volume," but the measurement of angles is so important a part of building geometry that the subject must be considered before proceeding to the solution of even the simplest problems.

Consider Fig. 1. Suppose the straight line OA to turn about the extremity O, keeping always in the surface (or plane) of the paper, through the positions marked OA^1, OA^2, OA^3, OA^4, OA^5, and back to its original position OA. Then, during the process of turning, the line has been—at successive instants— parallel to every straight line that may be drawn on the paper ; that is, the line has made every change of direction from its original position that is possible in the plane of the paper.

Now these changes of direction cannot be expressed in units of either length, area, or volume, since the

length of the line does not affect its direction; therefore
a special unit is required for angular measure; and
since every point in the revolving line traces out a
plane circle, any such circle may be divided into a
number of equal parts to represent equal changes in
the direction of the revolving line. When the circle
is divided into 360 equal parts each part is called a

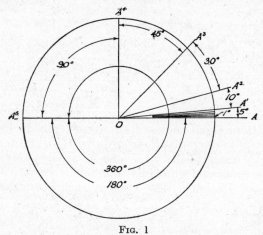

Fig. 1

degree; the degree is the most generally used unit of
angular measure, and is indicated by a small circle,
thus: $1° = 1$ degree. One sixtieth part of a degree is
called a *minute*, and one sixtieth part of a minute is
called a *second*.

In practical drawing a great many angles may be
set out direct with set-squares. Set-squares are thin
celluloid or wooden triangles similar to Figs. 2 and 3,
and vary in size from 3 in. or 4 in. sided, to over 12 in.
sided. The 45° set-square shown in Fig. 2 has one
angle of 90° and two angles of 45° each; therefore the
two sides that contain the right angle are equal in

length. The 60° set square, Fig. 3, also has one right angle and in addition one 30° angle and one 60° angle. By using the set-squares separately and combined, straight lines may be drawn through the centre of a given circle, so as to divide the complete circle into

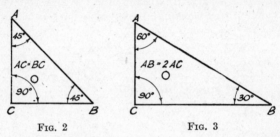

FIG. 2   FIG. 3

twenty-four equal angles of 15° each. Thus, in Fig, 4, the straight lines radiating from *o* are drawn at intervals of 15° by means of the " T "- and set-squares only, and may be continued through *o* to obtain a second twelve angles of 15° each. The student should be able to

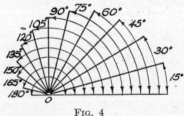

FIG. 4

repeat the figure by the method explained after noting that 45° − 30° = 15°, 45° + 30° = 75°, 60° + 45° = 105°, and similarly for the remaining angles involving the two set-squares.

Another important use of the set-squares is that of drawing parallels and perpendiculars in the manner

indicated in Fig. 5. Thus, to draw parallels and perpendiculars to the given
line *AB*, place the
longest edges of the
two set-squares to-
gether and turn them
until a third edge co-
incides with the given
line, as shown in the
figure, where *pqr* is the
45° square and *mno* the
60° square. If now the
45° square be held
firmly in position while
the other square is
moved along it into

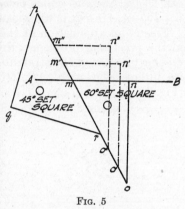

FIG. 5

required positions, as *m'n'o'* and *m"n"o"*, the side *mn*
will always be parallel, and *n o* perpendicular to *AB*.

ELEMENTARY PROBLEMS AND CONSTRUCTIONS

*To draw the perpendicular bisector of a given straight
line.* (Fig. 6.)

Let *AB* be the given straight line. Take a distance

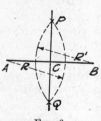

FIG. 6

greater than half *AB* in the com-
passes and, with *A* and *B* as successive centres, draw circular arcs to
intersect in points *P* and *Q*. Then,
since the radii *R* and *R'* are equal,
the distances *AQ*, *BQ*, *AP*, and *BP*
are all equal, and since any other
two equal intersecting arcs centered
in *A* and *B* respectively will also
intersect on the straight line through

P and *Q*, this straight line is perpendicular to *AB* and
its intersection *C* is the mid-point of *AB*.

Given any straight line AB, and any two points P and Q, the line and points being in one plane, to find a point O in AB that is equidistant from P and Q.

This is an application of the construction explained in the preceding problem; thus, if *OS* is the perpendicular bisector of the straight line distance *PQ*, and *O* its intersection with *AB*, *O* is the required point. (Fig. 7.)

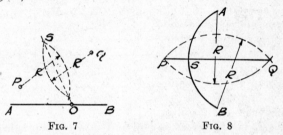

FIG. 7   FIG. 8

To draw the normal bisector of a given circular arc. (Fig. 8.)

Let *AB* be the given arc. Draw the perpendicular bisector of the straight line distance *AB*, as *PQ*, cutting the arc in *S*; then *PQ* is a normal to the arc and the point *S* is the mid-point of the arc.

To draw the bisector of a given angle. (Fig. 9.)

Let *AOB* be the given angle. With *O* as centre, and with any suitable radius, draw a circular arc to cut *AO* and *BO* in *Q* and *S* respectively, and draw the normal bisector of the arc *QS*. Thus, *PO* is the normal bisector of the arc *QS* and *T* is the mid-point of the arc, therefore the angles *TOS*, *TOQ* are equal, and *PO* bisects the angle *AOB*.

To bisect a given angle when the point of intersection between the arms of the angle is inaccessible. (Fig. 10.)

Let *AB* and *CD* be the given straight lines containing the angle to be bisected. Draw any straight line to intersect the given lines in H and G respectively. Draw the bisectors of the angles CGH, AHG to intersect in M, and draw the bisectors of the angles BHG, DGH to intersect in N; then the straight line EF through M and N is the required bisector.

The student will better appreciate the nature of this construction after considering some of the preceding problems as examples of simple loci, and it will be found

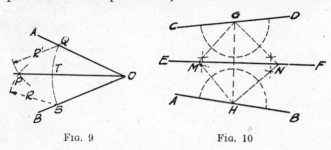

Fig. 9   Fig. 10

that by regarding elementary constructions in this way they become a matter of reasoning rather than remembering. Thus, reverting to Fig. 6, the straight line PQ may be regarded as the locus of all the points equidistant from the points A and B. Again, in Fig. 8, PQ is the locus of all points equidistant from A and B. In Fig. 9, OP is the locus of all points equidistant from the straight lines AO and BO. Similarly, in Fig. 10, EF is the locus of all points equidistant from CD and AB; for, GM is the locus of all points equidistant from GC and GH, and HM is the locus of all points equidistant from AH and GH; but M is in both loci, therefore, because its distances from CG and GH are equal, and its distances from AH and GH are equal, its distances from CG and AH are also equal. In the same way N may be proved equidistant from GD and HB.

SIMILAR FIGURES

Two figures are said to be similar when the corresponding angles of the figures are equal and the ratio between any two sides in one of the figures is equal to the ratio between the corresponding sides of the other figure.

This definition may be modified when applied to triangles, since two triangles having the corresponding

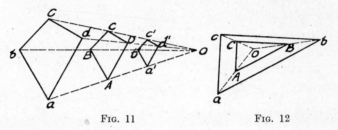

FIG. 11   FIG. 12

angles equal have equal ratios between corresponding sides.

The usual method of constructing similar figures is based upon this property of the triangle, and is known as the method of reducing and enlarging figures proportionally by similitude.

The method is shown in Fig. 11, and is as follows : Let *ABCD* be any given rectilineal plane figure, and let *O* be any point whatsoever. Then, if straight lines be drawn from *O* through the angular points of the figure, as shown, any figure having its sides parallel respectively to the sides *AB*, *BC*, *CD*, *DA*, each pair of corresponding angular points in the two figures being on the same radial from *O*, will be similar to the given figure. The figure nearer the pole will be the smaller figure, and the ratio of corresponding sides of the two figures will be equal to the ratio of the distances of the two figures from *O*.

In Fig. 12, the point O is within the figure, the latter being the triangle ABC. Since the sides of the second triangle abc are respectively parallel to the sides of ABC, and all the angular points of the triangles are in the radials from O, the two figures are similar and the ratio between corresponding sides is equal to the ratio of their distances from O.

In Fig. 13, the pole O is taken to be in an angular

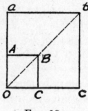
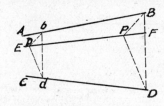

Fig. 13   Fig. 14

point of the given square, $OABC$, and the enlarged figure, $abcO$ is determined as before.

There are several practical uses of the construction just explained, apart from the enlargement and reduction of figures, one of which is illustrated in Fig. 14.

Given two converging straight lines—the point of intersection inaccessible—and given any point P, to draw a straight line through P to meet the given lines in their point of intersection.

Referring to Fig. 14. Let AB and CD be the given straight lines and let P be the given point. Draw any triangle, as PBD, having an angular point in each of the given lines and the third angular point in P, and draw a second triangle, as pbd, with sides parallel to PBD and an angular point in each of the given lines ; then the straight line through P and the corresponding angular point of the second triangle is the line required. Compare with Fig. 11.

To divide a given straight line into any number of equal parts. (Fig. 15.)

The construction is based on the following theorem—Any transversal of a system of parallel straight lines is divided by the parallels into equal segments.

Let it be required to divide the straight line AB (Fig. 15) *into, say, five equal parts.*

Draw the straight line *AD* to make any angle with *AB* and step any five equal divisions along *AD*, as

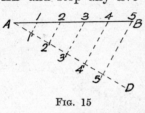

Fig. 15

$1'$, $2'$, $3'$, $4'$, $5'$. Join $5'$ to B and draw parallels to $5'B$ from the division points to obtain 1, 2, 3, 4, then the distances A–1, 1–2, 2–3, 3–4, and 4–5 are equal. Compare the figure with the theorem.

RECTILINEAR PLANE FIGURES

Figures bounded by straight lines and lying wholly in one plane are called rectilinear plane figures, and are named in accordance with the number of sides bounding the figures. Thus, a *triangle* has three sides ; a *quadrilateral* has four sides ; a *pentagon* has five sides ; a *hexagon* has six sides ; a *heptagon* has seven sides ; an *octagon* has eight sides ; a *nonagon* has nine sides; a *decagon* has ten sides ; an *undecagon* has eleven sides ; a *duodecagon* has 12 sides. Beyond twelve-sided, rectilinear plane figures are referred to as *polygons* of so many sides : as fifteen-sided polygon.

Polygons comprise two groups—" Regular " and " Irregular." A regular polygon has all its sides equal and all its angles equal ; all other polygons are irregular.

The sides and angles of a rectilinear plane figure are called " elements," and the data necessary to construct the figure of definite size and shape are : $2n - 3$ independent elements, where n equals the number of

sides of the figure : Thus, for a triangle n is 3, and
$2 \times 3 - 3 = 3$; for a quadrilateral n is 4, and $2 \times 4 - 3$
$= 5$; for a heptagon n is 7, and $2 \times 7 - 3 = 11$.

The qualification " independent " elements is necessary for the following reasons. Any polygon may be
divided into triangles, and the construction of the
polygon may always be regarded as the construction
of a series of triangles. But the sum of the angles of

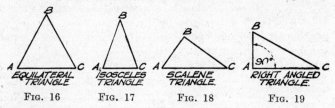

FIG. 16   FIG. 17   FIG. 18   FIG. 19

any triangle is 180°, and, therefore, two angles being
given, the third can only have one value. That is :
the magnitude of any one angle of a triangle is depen-
dent upon the magnitudes of the other two angles ;
then the angles are not independent elements. With
respect to the sides of the triangles, however, the length
of any one may be varied—within certain limits—
without affecting the lengths of the remaining sides ;
then the sides are independent elements.

Since a polygon may always be regarded as a number
of superimposed triangles, it is desirable to consider
the triangle in detail before proceeding further with
polygons.

Triangles. A triangle having three equal sides has
three equal angles and is called " equilateral." Since
the three angles are equal, each is 60° (Fig. 16).

A triangle having two equal sides has two equal
angles, and is called " Isosceles." The side to which
the equal angles are adjacent may be called the " base,"
and the angular point opposite that side may be called

the " vertex " or " apex." The perpendicular bisector of the base passes through the vertex (Fig. 17).

A triangle having no two equal sides has no two angles equal, and is called " Scalene " (Fig. 18).

A triangle having one of its angles a right angle is called a " Right-angled triangle " (Fig. 19).

In any triangle : any two sides are greater than the third side ; the greatest angle is opposite the greatest side ; the smallest angle is opposite the smallest side. If any side of a triangle be chosen as base, the perpendicular distance of the opposite angular point from the base is called the " altitude " or " height." The area of any triangle is equal to the base multiplied by half the altitude, or, Area $= \dfrac{\text{base} \times \text{height}}{2}$; from this it follows that : triangles on the same, or equal base, and between the same parallels, are equal in area ; the bisectors of the three angles of any triangle are concurrent. The perpendicular bisectors of the three sides are concurrent. The three straight lines, each perpendicular to one side and passing through the opposite angular point are concurrent.

(NOTE. Lines passing through the same point are said to be concurrent.)

There are five standard cases of data arrangement for the construction of ordinary triangles, as follows—

Given—(1) Three sides.

,, 　　(2) Two sides and the included angle.

,, 　　(3) Two sides and an opposite angle.

,, 　　(4) One side and the two adjacent angles.

,, 　　(5) One side, one adjacent, one opposite angle.

GEOMETRY AND SETTING-OUT

The student should prepare a table of actual data for the five cases, and then construct the triangles to

conform to the data. If it is found that one or more of
the cases cannot be constructed to the selected magnitudes, the error in the data will probably be found after
a reconsideration of the properties given above.

In the construction of right-angled triangles there
are nine data arrangements from which the figures may
be constructed, and since the right angle is always
understood without being
stated in the data table,
only the two additional
magnitudes require stat-
ing, and these may be any
one of the following : Let
the two sides forming the
right angle be called *base*
and *perpendicular*, and
indicated by *B* and *P*
respectively, and let the
hypotenuse, the longest
side, be indicated by *H*.
Also, let the vertical
angle and the base angle
be indicated by *α* and *β*

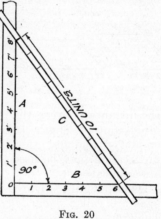

Fig. 20

(alpha and beta) respectively—Given (1) *B* and *P* ;
(2) *B* and *H* ; (3) *P* and *H* ; (4) *B* and *α* ; (5) *B* and
β ; (6) *P* and *α* ; (7) *P* and *β* ; (8) *H* and *α* ; (9) *H*
and *β*.

One of the most valuable practical properties of the
right-angled triangle is as follows : *If similar figures
be arranged in corresponding positions, one on each side
of the triangle, the area of the figure on the hypotenuse is
equal to the sum of the areas of the other two figures.*
Or, $H^2 = B^2 + P^2$; $H^2 - B^2 = P^2$; $H^2 - P^2 = B^2$.

A practical example will further explain this property.
Thus, let it be required to form or test a right angle
between two members in a large framing ; then, if

6 ft. be set off along one member and 8 ft. along the
other member—the two distances being measured from
a common point in the intersection of the members—
the opposite extremities of the two members, when the
angle is 90°, is 10 ft. Refer to Fig. 20. Let A and B
be the inner arrises of two members containing an
angle of 90° ; then, if 6 ft. be set off along B and 8 ft.
be set off along A, as shown at 06 and 08′ respectively,

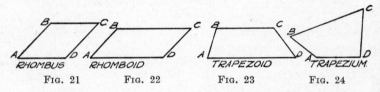

| FIG. 21 | FIG. 22 | FIG. 23 | FIG. 24 |

the distance between the points 6 and 8′ is 10 ft. Any
other unit of length, as inches, yards, etc., may be
employed, and any other three values of corresponding
progression may be used ; thus 3, 4, 5, or 12, 16, 20
are applicable.

Quadrilaterals. Figures bounded by four straight
lines are called *quadrilaterals*, or, for brevity, quads.
The group comprises the *square* (no figure), *rectangle* (no
figure), *rhombus* (Fig. 21), *rhomboid* (Fig. 22), *trapezoid*
(Fig. 23), and *trapezium* (Fig. 24).

The square and rectangle should require no explanation. The rhombus has four equal sides, equal opposite
angles, unequal adjacent angles, and the diagonals
bisect each other at right angles. The rhomboid has
its opposite sides equal, adjacent sides unequal, opposite angles equal, adjacent angles unequal, and the
diagonals bisect each other but not at right angles.

The trapezoid has one pair of opposite sides parallel,
but no fixed relationship between the other two sides,
the angles, or the diagonals. The trapezium has no
fixed relationship between its sides, angles, or diagonals.

(NOTE. The terms trapezoid and trapezium are interchanged by some geometers, but the applications given here are the more usual.)

Construction of Polygons. A regular pentagon and an irregular pentagon are shown in Figs. 25 and 26 respectively, and should serve to illustrate the difference between the two groups. The two properties that provide accurate methods of constructing any given

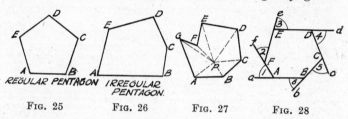

REGULAR PENTAGON   IRREGULAR PENTAGON.

Fig. 25   Fig. 26   Fig. 27   Fig. 28

polygon are shown in Figs. 27 and 28. Thus, if any given point within any polygon be joined by straight lines to all the angular points of the figure, the sum of the angles about the point equals 360°. In Fig. 27, P is the given point, and obviously, the sum of the angles, APB, BPC, CPD, DPE, EPF, FPG, and GPA is 360°. In Fig. 28, the following property is illustrated. The supplements of the interior angles of any polygon are together equal to 360°. The supplement of the interior angle is usually called the " exterior angle," and is the angle between one side of the figure and the adjacent side produced ; thus, in the figure, the angles 1, 2, 3, 4, 5, and 6 are the exterior angles, and it is easily shown that they are together equal to four right angles or 360°.

To inscribe any given regular polygon in any given circle. (Fig. 29.)

Since the sides of a regular polygon are equal, the angles subtended by the sides at the centre of the

figure are also equal. Further, the centre of a regular
polygon inscribed in a circle is the centre of the circle.
Then, by the property illustrated in Fig. 27, any polygon may be inscribed in a given circle by setting out
the required number of equal angles about the centre
of the circle, each angle being made equal to 360°
divided by the number of sides. Thus, in Fig. 29, if *n*

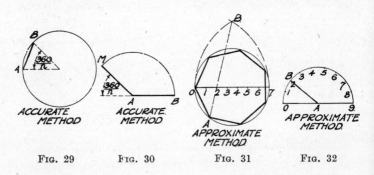

ACCURATE	ACCURATE	APPROXIMATE	APPROXIMATE
METHOD	METHOD.	METHOD	METHOD.
Fig. 29	Fig. 30	Fig. 31	Fig. 32

equals the number of sides in the required polygon, and
AB subtends an angle of 360° divided by *n*, as shown,
then *AB* is one side of the required polygon, and will
divide the circumference of the circle into the required
number of equal parts.

*To erect any given regular polygon on any given
straight line as one side.* (Fig. 30.)

Let *AB* be the given side. Then, by the property
illustrated in Fig. 28, if *AM* be drawn equal to *AB* and
to make an angle with *AB* produced equal to 360°
divided by the number of sides, *AM* is a second side
of the required polygon. The figure may now be
completed by drawing a circle to pass through *M*,
A, and *B* and stepping the length *AB* around the
circumference.

Approximate methods of constructing regular polygons.

To inscribe any given regular polygon in any given circle. (Fig. 31.)

Let the required polygon be a heptagon, and let 07 be a diameter of the given circle. Divide 07 into seven equal parts, as 0–1, 1–2, . . . 6–7. With the diameter as radius, draw circular arcs centred in 0 and 7, and intersecting in *B*. Draw a straight line through *B* and 2 to cut the circumference in *A*, and join *A* to 0 ; then *A*0 is the length of side required and may be stepped around the circumference of the circle to complete the figure.

(NOTE. The construction is capable of giving a close approximation only, and point 2 is utilized in the manner shown in every case.)

To erect a given regular polygon on a given straight line. (Fig. 32.)

Let *A*9 be the given side, and let a nonagon be the required figure. With *A* as centre, *A*9 as radius, draw the semicircle 09, and divide the circumference into nine equal divisions, marking the division points, 1, 2, 3, . . . 8. Then the straight line *A*2 is the second side in length and direction (approx.).

The construction of any irregular polygon consists of constructing a number of superimposed triangles, and the rules governing the data arrangements for triangles are equally applicable to irregular polygons. Great care is, however, necessary to avoid ambiguity and redundancy in the selection of data ; the only certain method is that of dividing the polygon into triangles, and then considering each separate triangle to ensure that all the selected elements are independent, and that the number involved in each triangle is in accordance with the rule, $2n - 3$.

THE CIRCLE

A *circle* is a plane area bounded by a line called the

circumference, all points in this line being equidistant from the centre of the area. In Fig. 33 the parts of a circle are illustrated and named. Thus : any straight line through the centre of the circle and having its extremities in the circumference is called a *diameter* ; any straight line joining the centre to the circumference is a *radius* ; any straight line not through the centre, but with its extremities in the circumference, is a

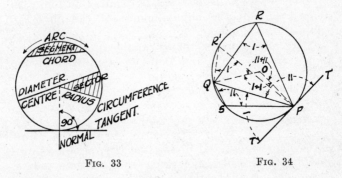

Fig. 33   Fig. 34

chord ; any part of the circumference is an *arc* ; any straight line directed towards the centre, and in the plane of the circle, is a *normal* ; any straight line touching, but not cutting the circumference, is a *tangent* ; any part of a circle bounded by an arc and a chord is a *segment* ; any part of a circle bounded by an arc and two radii is a *sector*.

(NOTE. The terms circle, segment, and sector refer to areas ; the remaining terms refer to lines. Also, a normal may be wholly within, wholly without, or partly inside and partly outside the circle ; thus, a radius is a normal, but a normal is not necessarily a radius. Further, a normal and a tangent at the same point in the circumference contain an angle of 90°.)

Angles in a Segment. (Fig. 34.) The following

properties of the circle must be carefully considered, since they are involved in the solutions of many practical problems : *The angle in a segment is constant ;* thus, let *PQ*, Fig. 34, be any chord of the circle, centre *O* ; then the angles *PRQ* and *PR'Q* are equal—*R* and *R'* being any points whatsoever in the circumference of the arc of the segment on *PQ*. Similarly, *QSP* is the angle in the segment on the opposite side of *PQ*, and is constant for every position of *S* in the arc *PSQ*.

The angle in a semicircle is a right angle. When the segment is greater than a semicircle the angle is acute, when less than a semicircle, the angle is obtuse.

The angle at the centre of a circle is twice that at the circumference ; thus (Fig. 34), the obtuse angle *QOP*—marked 1 + 1—is equal to twice the angle *QRP*—marked 1 ; also the reflex angle *QOP*—marked 11 + 11 —is equal to twice the angle *QSP*—marked 11. From this it follows that the opposite angles of any quadrilateral inscribed in a circle are supplementary.

If any chord be drawn from the point of contact of any tangent, the angle between the chord and the tangent is equal to the angle in the opposite segment ; thus (Fig. 34), if *TT'* be a tangent to the circle at *P*, the angles *QPT* and *QRP* are equal, and the angles *QPT'* and *QSP* are equal.

Problems Involving the Foregoing Properties. *Given any two points, P and Q, and any straight line, AB, to draw straight lines from P and Q to intersect on AB and contain a given angle.* (Fig. 35.)

Join *P* to *Q* and draw *QT* to make the given angle with *PQ*. Draw a perpendicular to *QT* from *Q* to intersect the perpendicular bisector of *PQ* in *O*. With *O* as centre, draw the arc on *PQ* to intersect *AB* in *M* and *N*. Then the straight lines from *M* to *P* and *Q* is one solution, and the straight lines *NP*, *NQ* is a second solution. Compare with Fig. 34.

To cut off from a given circle a segment to contain a given angle. (Fig. 36.)

Let *OD* be a radius of the given circle. Draw the tangent *DT* at right angles to *DO*, and draw *DQ* to make the given angle with *DT*; then *QRD* is the required segment, and the angles *QDT*, *QRD* are equal.

Given the arc of a circle, the centre being inaccessible

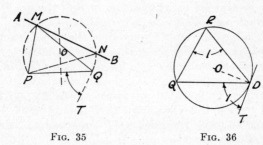

FIG. 35   FIG. 36

to draw a tangent at, or near, the extremity of the arc. (Fig. 37.)

Let *AB* be the given arc. Draw the chord *AB*, and draw straight lines from *A* and *B* through any point *C* in the arc. Draw *TA*, making the angle *TAC* equal to the angle *ABC*; then *TA* is the required tangent; for, the angle between the chord *AC* and the tangent *AT* is equal to the angle *ABC* in the opposite segment.

Geometrical Mean. The graphical determination of the geometrical mean, or *mean proportional*, is of great practical importance, since it is necessary in the solutions of many problems on tangential lines and circles. Stated numerically, the geometrical mean of two quantities is the square root of the product of the quantities; thus, the mean proportional of 4 and 9 is 6; for $4 \times 9 = 36$ and 6×6, or $6^2 = 36$, or $\sqrt{4 \times 9} = 6$. The construction for the graphical

determination of the geometrical mean is illustrated
in Fig. 38, and is as follows—

Let the straight lines PQ and QR, when measured
by the same unit, represent two given quantities.
Draw a semicircle on PR, and draw a perpendicular
to PR from Q to cut the circumference of the semicircle
in S' ; then, if QS' be also measured by the same unit,

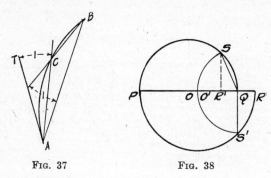

FIG. 37   FIG. 38

it will equal the required geometrical mean between
the given quantities. Experiment as follows : Draw
PQ equal to $2\frac{1}{4}$ in., and QR equal to 1 in. ; then QS'
will equal $1\frac{1}{2}$ in. ; for if $\frac{1}{4}$ in. be the selected unit,
$PQ = 9$ units, $QR = 4$ units, and $QS' = 6$ units.

A second method, shown in the same figure, is more
compact and, usually, more convenient for practical
applications. Thus, if PQ equals one quantity as
before, and QR' equals the second quantity, but
measured towards instead of away from P, then the
perpendicular to PQ from R' to meet the semicircle
on PQ is S, gives QS equal to QS', equals the geometrical
mean as before.

The value of the above construction will be better
appreciated after a consideration of a further property
of the circle illustrated in Fig. 39. Thus : *if from any*

*point P outside a circle two straight lines be drawn, one
to cut the circumference in points Q and R, the other to
touch it in a point T, PT is the geometrical mean between
PR and PQ.* Referring to the figure, let P be any point
outside the given circle ; let PT be a tangent touching
the circle at T ; let PQR be any line from P to cut
the circle in points Q and R ; then $\overline{PT^2} = \overline{PR} \times \overline{PQ}$.

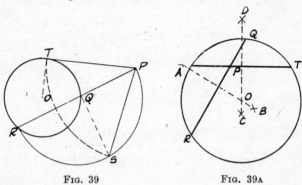

FIG. 39   FIG. 39A

Applying the construction illustrated in Fig. 38 :
draw the semicircle on PR, as shown, and draw QS
perpendicular to PR ; then PS equals PT. The solutions to several problems involving this property and
construction are given later.

Chords and Segments. *The perpendicular bisector of
any chord of a circle passes through the centre of the circle.*
(Fig. 39A.)

Referring to the figure : Let QR and ST be any two
chords of the circle, centre O ; then the extremities,
Q, R, S, T of the chords are equidistant from O, and
the perpendicular bisectors AB and CD of the chords
intersect in O.

*The product of the segments of concurrent chords of a
circle is constant.* (Fig. 39A.)

Thus, in the figure, $\overline{SP} \times \overline{TP} = \overline{RP} \times \overline{QP} =$ the product of the segments of any other chord through P.

An example of the uses of the properties illustrated in Fig. 39A is given in Fig. 40. Let AB be the given span, CD the given rise of a segmental arch. Then, when the centre O is accessible, it may be found by drawing the

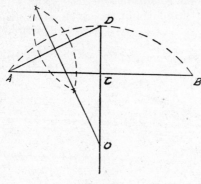

Fig. 40

perpendicular bisectors of AB and AD to intersect in O as shown.

In examples where the centre is so remote that the graphical method of finding it is inconvenient, the radius may be determined by a calculation based upon the property of concurrent chords, thus : $\overline{AC} \times \overline{CB} = \overline{CD}(2r - \overline{CD})$; where r is the required radius. But $AC = CB$; therefore, $\overline{AC^2} = \overline{CD}(2r - \overline{CD})$.

By transposal, $\dfrac{\overline{AC^2}}{\overline{CD}} = 2r - \overline{CD}, = \dfrac{\overline{AC^2}}{\overline{CD}} + \overline{CD} = 2r,$

$= \dfrac{\overline{AC^2} + \overline{CD^2}}{2\overline{CD}}.$ But $\overline{AC^2} + \overline{CD^2} = \overline{AD^2}$; therefore,

$\dfrac{\overline{AD^2}}{2\overline{CD}} = r.$ Substituting definite values : Let $AC = 2$ in.

and $CD = 1$ in. Then $\overline{AC^2} = 4$, $\overline{CD^2} = 1$. Therefore, $\overline{AD^2} = 5$, and $\dfrac{\overline{AD^2}}{2\overline{CD}} = \dfrac{5}{2}$, $= 2\frac{1}{2}$ in. $=$ the required radius.

Tangents to Circles. *To draw tangents to a circle from any point P outside the circle.* (Fig. 41.)

Let O be the centre of the given circle, and P be the

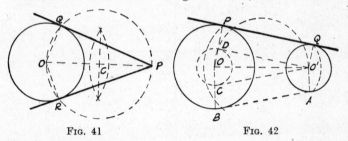

FIG. 41   FIG. 42

given point. Draw the straight line OP and bisect it in C. With C as centre, describe a circle through O and P to cut the circumference of the given circle in points R and Q. Then straight lines from P through R and Q will be the required tangents, and R and Q will be the points of contact.

(NOTE. Since each of the angles PRO and PQO is an angle in a semicircle, they are right angles, and satisfy the condition relating to a tangent and normal drawn to the same point in the circumference of a circle.)

To draw the common tangents to two given circles. (Figs. 42 and 43.)

First, when the given circles are required to be on the same side of the tangent, as in Fig. 42. Let O and O' be the centres, and OB and $O'A$ the radii respectively of the given circles. Let $O'A$ and OB be any pairs of parallel radii, and let $O'C$ be parallel to AB. With O as centre, OC as radius, draw a circle, and draw tangents to this circle from O' ; one such tangent is shown at O, D, D being its point of contact. Draw OD and produce to P, and draw $O'Q$ parallel to OP. Then P and Q are the points of contact of one of the required tangents, and the second tangent may be determined in a similar manner.

When the given circles cut one another, only two common tangents may be drawn. When the given

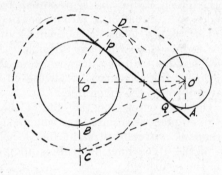

Fig. 43

circles touch one another, three common tangents may be drawn. When the given circles are apart from one another, four common tangents may be drawn ; two as in Fig. 42, and two as in Fig. 43.

Referring to the latter figure, where PQ is a common tangent, the construction will be best explained by comparison with the preceding example. Thus, in Fig. 42, the radius of the circle OC is equal to the difference between the radii of the given circles, whereas in Fig. 43 the radius of the circle OC is equal to the sum of the radii of the given circles. In all other respects the constructions are identical. The principle of the solution is also common to both cases and should be apparent.

Problems on Tangential Arcs and Lines. *Given any*
straight line AB and any point P, to draw a circle of
given radius to touch the given line and pass through the
given point. (Fig. 44.)

This problem, and several subsequent ones, is introduced to present the opportunity of explaining how
certain solutions may be argued from the fundamental
constructions and principles involved in the problem.
Thus, if the given radius be represented by x, the
circumference of a circle of x radius, centred in the
given point P, is the locus of the centres of all the
circles of x radius that will pass through P. Also, a
straight line parallel to, and x distance from, the given
line is the locus of the centres of all the circles of x
radius that will touch the given line.

(NOTE. Only the circles on the side of the line on
which the given point is situated are being considered ;
actually there is a second straight line locus on the
other side of the given line, but this is obviously not
involved in the solution.)

Referring now to Fig. 44 : *CD* is parallel to, and
x distance from *AB* and, therefore, contains the required
centre, and the circle of x radius centred in P cuts *CD*
in the point O. Then O is the centre of a circle of x
radius that will pass through P and touch *AB*. There
is a second centre that may be determined by continuing
the arc, centre P, to cut *CD* a second time.

To determine a circle of given radius to touch a given
straight and touch a given circle. (Fig. 45.)

Let *AB* be the given line and O the centre of the
given circle, and let x represent the given radius.
Then, if *CD* be parallel to and x distance from *AB*, it
will contain the centres of all the circles of x radius
that will touch *AB*. If, now, any radius, as *OE*, of
the given circle be produced to F, making *EF* equal x,
and a circle with centre O, radius *OF*, be drawn, the

circumference of this circle will contain the centres of all the circles of x radius that will touch the given circle. Then the points of intersection between CD and the circumference of the circle OF (only one O' is shown), are the centres of the two circles which satisfy the given conditions. Draw $O'P$ perpendicular to AB, and join O to O'; then P is the point of contact

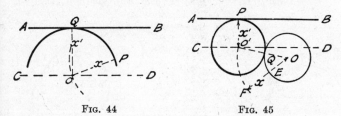

Fig. 44   Fig. 45

between the required circle and the given straight line, and Q is the point of contact between the required circle and the given circle.

(NOTE. The points of contact are of the greatest importance in practical applications of arcs and lines—as will be seen later—and should always be determined before the tangential arc or line is drawn.)

Given any three straight lines, one of which cuts each of the other two—one or more produced if necessary—to draw the circles that will touch the three given lines tangentially. (Fig. 46.)

Let AB, BC, and CD be the given straight lines. Draw the bisectors of the angles ABC and BCD to intersect in O. Then BO is the locus of the centres of the circles that will touch AB and BC; and CO is the locus of the centres of the circles that will touch BC and CD. Therefore, O is the centre of the circle that will touch AB, BC, and CD. Draw OP, OQ, and OR perpendicular to AB, BC, and CD respectively; then P, Q, and R are the points of contact.

Draw *BO'* and *CO'* perpendicular to *BO* and *CO* respectively ; then *O'* is the centre of a circle that will touch *BC*, *AB* (produced), and *DC* (produced), and *R*, *S*, and *T* are the points of contact.

(NOTE. The bisectors of the adjacent angles of any two intersecting straight lines are at right angles to one another.)

Given any circle, centre O, and any straight line AB

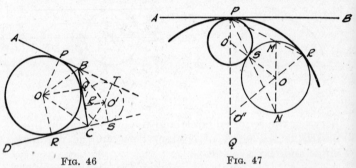

| FIG. 46 | FIG. 47 |

containing any given point P, to draw the circles that will touch AB at P and touch the given circle. (Fig. 47.)

Draw *PQ* perpendicular to *AB* ; then the centres of all the circles that will touch *AB* at *P* are in *PQ*. Draw *MN* through *O* parallel to *PQ*, and draw straight lines from *P* through *M* and *N* to cut the circumference of the given circle in points *R* and *S* respectively.

Draw straight lines through *RO* and *OS* to cut *PQ* in points *O''* and *O'* respectively ; then *O'* and *O''* are the centres of the required circles. For, since *OM* and *OR* are radii of the same circle, the triangle *OMR* is isosceles ; and since *P* is in *RM* produced, *O''* in *RO* produced, and *O''P* is parallel to *OM*, *O''PR* is also isosceles ; and because *R* is in the straight line through the centres *O''* and *O*, a circle centred in *O''* and of radius *O''P* will touch the given circle tangentially in

R. Similarly, because *ONS* is isosceles, *O'PS* is also isosceles ; and since *S* is in the straight line joining the centres *O* and *O'*, a circle, centre *O'*, radius *O'P* will touch the given circle tangentially in *S*.

(NOTE. This construction may be proved by the similar triangles, as above, but may only be logically argued by reference to centres of "similitude," which are outside the scope of this work.)

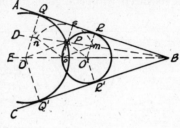

Given any two straight lines AB and BC, and any point P between the lines, to draw circles to pass through P and touch the given straight lines. (Fig. 48.)

FIG. 48

Draw *BE* to bisect the angle between the given lines ; then *BE* is the locus of the centres of all the circles that will touch *AB* and *BC*. Draw *BD* through the given point *P* and draw *os* through *P* and perpendicular to *AB*. With *o* as centre, *os* as radius, draw a circular arc to cut *BD* in points *m* and *n*. Join *o* to *m* and to *n*, and draw parallels to *om* and *on* from *P* to intersect *BE* in *O* and *O'* respectively. Then *O* and *O'* are the centres of the required circles. This construction may be proved by reference to Fig. 11 and the matter relating thereto. Thus, the figures *OQP* and *osm* are similar, and the figures *O'RP* and *osn* are similar, since corresponding points in each pair of similar figures are in the same radials from *B*.

(NOTE. *os* is not necessarily drawn through *P*.)

Given any straight line AB and any two points P and Q, on the same side of the line, to draw circles to pass through the given points and touch the given straight line. (Fig. 49.)

Draw a straight line through Q and P to meet AB in point R, and draw CD to bisect PQ perpendicularly. Then the centre of any circle to pass through P and Q is in CD, and the length of the tangent from R to any circle that will pass through P and Q is equal to the geometrical mean between RQ and RP. But AB is required to be tangent to the circles through P and

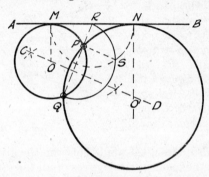

Fig. 49

Q; therefore the points of contact between AB and the required circles will each be distant from R an amount equal to the geometrical mean between RP and RQ. Draw a semicircle on RQ, and from P draw a parallel to CD to cut the circumference of the semi-circle in S. With R as centre, RS as radius, cut AB in M and N. Then M and N are the points of contact, and the required centres O and O' are the points of intersection between CD and perpendiculars to AB from M and N respectively.

Given any circle, centre O, and any two points, P and Q, both within or both without the circle, to draw the circles that will pass through the given points and touch the given circle. (Fig. 50.)

Draw CD to bisect, perpendicularly, the straight

line joining P to Q. With any suitable point o in CD as centre, draw a circle to pass through P and Q and cut the circumference of the given circle in points S and R. Draw a straight line through S and R to meet QP produced in T. Then, since SR and PQ are chords of the same circle, centre o, and SR is also a chord of the given circle, the length of tangents from T to the

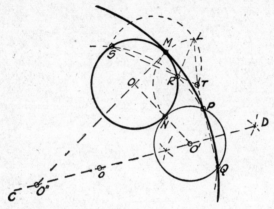

Fig. 50

given circle, and to any circle that may be drawn through P and Q, is equal to the geometrical mean between TS and TR, or between TP and TQ; this length, determined as before, is shown at TL. With T as centre, TL as radius, cut the given circle in the points M and N, and draw straight lines ON and MO to cut CD in points O' and O'' respectively. Then O' and O'' are the required centres, and N and M the points of contact.

(NOTE. Straight lines from T to M and N are the common tangents to the given circle and a required circle.)

Practical Applications of Tangential Arcs and Lines.
The methods of finding the centres for drawing the
curved portions of the outline of the handrail section,
Fig. 51, are indicated by the construction lines on the
left of the figure. In each case the construction is

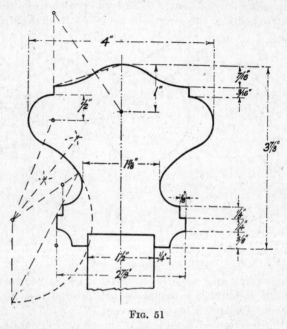

FIG. 51

identical with that in one or the other of the foregoing
solutions. The student should draw the figure to the
given dimensions, referring to the preceding figures for
guidance if necessary.

*Given the span and rise of a false elliptical arch, to
construct the curve with three tangential circular arcs.*
(Fig. 52.)

Any one of the following conditions may be given

in addition to those stated in the problem : The curve
shall contain at least five points contained by the true
elliptical arc ; the radius of the crown curve may be
given ; the radius of the springing curve may be given.

Let AC be the given span and DB the given rise.
Complete the rectangle $AEFC$ and bisect AE in m.
Draw a straight line from A to make $45°$ with AC, and

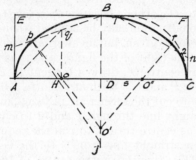

Fig. 52

meet mB in q. From q draw a line to meet AC perpendicularly in o. With o as centre, oA as radius,
draw a circular arc to cut mB in p. Draw a straight
line through p and o to meet BD produced in O' ; then
O' is the centre of the tangential arc pB.

This method, devised by the writer, always gives
the point p in, or very near to, the true elliptical curve.
Thus, if DJ be equal to DB and AH be half AD, the
point of intersection between mB and JH produced
will be actually in the true ellipse, and the figure gives
some indication of how nearly this point is to p. Also,
since it will be shown that either the larger or the
smaller radius may be given, the curve may be made
to pass through any one point in the true curve intermediate between A and B ; hence, a second point in
the section of the curve to the right of DB, together

with the points A, B, and C, gives five points of the false curve coincident with points in the true curve.

Now let the lower radius be any given length within the limits of the rectangle. Same figure. Make Ao equal to the given radius, erect a perpendicular to AC from o and draw the arc through A to cut the perpendicular in q. From B draw a straight line through q to cut the arc in p, and from p draw a straight line through o to O'. Then, because $op = oq$, $O'p = O'B$. The same construction may be applied when the radius of the upper arc is given, but an alternative construction is shown on the right of the figure, and is as follows :

About any centre O', draw a tangent to EF at B to pass between F and C. With any centre S in DC draw a second arc to cut the former arc in two points 1 and 2. Draw a straight line through 1 and 2 to cut FC in n, and with n as centre turn C to r in the required upper arc. Draw a straight line from r to the centre O' to cut DC in O''; then O'' is the centre of the required lower arc. For, nC is the geometrical mean between $n1$ and $n2$, therefore r is the point of contact of a tangent to the upper arc from n, and nr is the length of the tangent from n to any arc drawn tangent to FC at C. Then r is the point of contact of a tangent from n common to both arcs, and, therefore, the arcs intersect tangentially in point r.

To draw a scroll curve of circular quadrants, given the radius of the eye and the distances between the tangents at the extremities of each convolution. (Fig. 53.)

The circle into which the inner end of the volute, or scroll curve, finishes tangentially, is called the *eye* of the volute. One complete turn of a scroll curve is called a *convolution*.

Let O be the centre and OA the given radius of the eye. Then the first convolution may be regarded as starting at A and finishing at E, and the distance

between the parallel tangents at *A* and *E* may be any
given distance.

The number of ways in which the centres may be
arranged to give the required distance between the
tangents at *A* and *E* is infinite, but each arrangement
will conform to the following simple law : *The distance
between the tangents at the extremities of a convolution is*

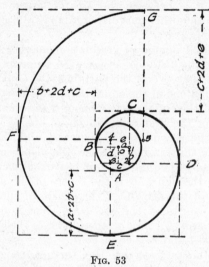

Fig. 53

*equal to the first radial increase plus twice the second
radial increase plus the third radial increase.*

The reason for this is as follows : The first and third
centre displacements are parallel to the tangents, and
therefore do not affect the distance between the tangents ; the second centre displacement is perpendicular
to, and towards the tangents, and therefore directly
affects the distance between them ; and, since the
displacements equal the radial increases, the distance
between the tangents is as stated. It will be seen, then,

that if the distance between the tangents be divided into four equal parts, the required centres may be arranged in the angular points of a square having each side equal to one of the parts. The reason why this simple arrangement is considered unsatisfactory in large scroll curves is that the effect of a uniform radial increase is more apparent between the arcs of smaller radii than it is between the arcs of larger radii, and therefore a smoother curve is obtained from graduated radial increases.

Any desired degree of graduation may be obtained by dividing the distance between the tangents into four parts, such that two of the parts may be equal, a third part less than one of the equal parts, the fourth greater than one of the equal parts. Then, if the smallest part be taken for the first radial increase, one of the equal parts for the second radial increase, and the largest part for the third radial increase, the distance between the tangents will equal the four parts together.

Thus, in the figure, O is the centre of the arc AB, 1 the centre of the arc BC, 2 the centre of the arc CD, and 3 the centre of the arc DE. Then if $0-1 = a$, $1-2 = b$, and $2-3 = c$, the distance between the tangents at A and E is equal to $a + 2b + c$.

The distances between the further tangents are indicated algebraically in the same manner, and should be referred to the corresponding distances between the centres.

CONIC SECTIONS
The Ellipse

The *ellipse* is one of the principal conic sections, and is directly involved in many practical building problems, particularly in the work of the joiner or carpenter ; thus, a knowledge of the ellipse is necessary in the construction of certain types of centres and centering, conical roofs, voids in pitched roofs, geometrical stairs and handrails, work of double curvature, etc.

The ellipse may be considered as a section of a right circular cone by a plane inclined to the axis and cutting every generator of the solid, on one side of the vertex, or, as the locus of a point moving in a plane so that the ratio of its distances from a fixed point and fixed straight line in the plane is constant and less than unity.

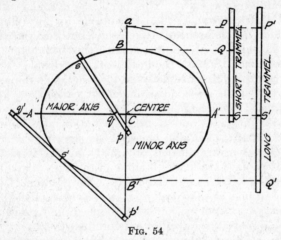

Fig. 54

Methods of Constructing the Ellipse. One of the best practical methods of constructing an elliptical curve is called the *trammel method*. (Fig. 54.) The ellipse is symmetrical about two straight lines which bisect each other in the centre of the figure, and these lines are called the *axes* of the ellipse; the longer being the *major axis*, the shorter the *minor axis*. Thus, in the figure, AA' and BB' are the major and minor axes respectively.

Produce $B'B$ to a, making Ca equal to CA'; then any straight line containing the three points constitutes a trammel, such that if the point *a* is made to move always in the minor axis, and *B* to move always in the major axis, *C* will trace out the elliptic curve.

Let *PQS* be a strip of paper, wood, or other suitable material placed parallel to *aBC*. Then, if *a*, *B*, and *C* be projected parallel to *P*, *Q*, and *S* respectively, the strip may be placed on the axes, as shown at *pqs*, and moved into successive positions to obtain any number of points in the curve. This particular form is called the " short trammel," and is suitable for any ellipse in which the difference between the lengths of the axes is sufficiently great, compared with the total length of the trammel, to make accurate working possible.

When the difference between the lengths of the axes is unduly small, a second arrangement, called the " long trammel," is more efficient. Again, referring to Fig. 54. If the points *a*, *C*, and *B'* be projected or marked on a second strip of suitable material, as shown at *P'*, *S'*, and *Q'*, a long trammel is obtained. In this form the outside points are made to move in the axes, while the inside point traces out the curve. One position of the long trammel is shown at *p'*, *q'*, *s'*—*q'* being always in the major axis, or major axis produced, and *p* always in the minor axis, or minor axis produced.

The student should practice with trammels for ellipses of various lengths of axes to gain proficiency in manipulating the trammels.

Given the semi-minor axis CB and a point P in the curve, to determine the trammel. (Fig. 55.)

This is the form in which the data for drawing the face mould curves in geometrical handrailing are usually presented. Draw the line of major axis through *C* perpendicular to *CB*. Make *PQ* equal to *BC*. Produce *PQ* and *BC* to meet in *R*. Then *PQR* is the required trammel in the position at the instant of tracing the curve through *P*.

To inscribe an ellipse in a rectangle by intersecting straight lines. (Fig. 56.)

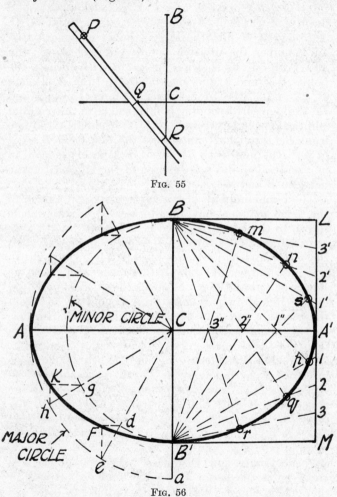

FIG. 55

FIG. 56

AA' and BB' are the major and minor axes respectively. Considering only the half of the figure to the right of BB, draw BL and $B'M$ parallel to CA', and draw LM through A' parallel to BB'. Divide CA', $A'L$, and $A'M$ into the same number of equal parts, and number the division points 1, 2, 3 ; 1', 2', 3' ; and 1'', 2'', 3'', as shown. Then if B' be joined to the points 1, 2, and 3, and lines be drawn from B through 1'', 2'', and 3'', the intersections of the lines from B and B', through corresponding points, will be in the required elliptical curve between A' and B'. Similarly, the line from B', through 2'', intersects the line from B to 2' in n ; $B'1''$ intersects $B1'$ in s ; $B'3''$ intersects $B3'$ in m ; and m, n, and s are points in the elliptical curve between B and A'.

The remaining half of the curve may be obtained in the same manner, but an alternative construction is shown to the left of BB' and is as follows : With C as centre draw circles through B and A—these are called the *minor* and *major circles* respectively. Draw any— and any number of—radials to cut the two circles as shown at Cde and Cgh. From the points d and g in the minor circle draw parallels to the major axis, and from the points e and h in the major circle draw parallels to the minor axis ; the intersections F and K are points in the required curve.

Conjugate Diameters. (Fig. 57.) When an ellipse is inscribed in a rhomboid, as shown in the figure, the straight lines aa' and bb' through the centre joining the mid-points of each pair of parallel sides are not the principal axes, but are called *conjugate diameters*. The curve is tangent to the sides of the rhomboid at the mid-points aa' and bb'.

Focal Points and Distances. (Fig. 58.) Let AA' and BB' be the major and minor axes respectively of the given ellipse. With CA as radius, B or B' as centre, cut AA' in points F and F'. Then F and F' are called the *foci* or *focal points*—each being a *focus* —of the ellipse, and are such that, if any point P in the curve be joined to them by straight lines, the two

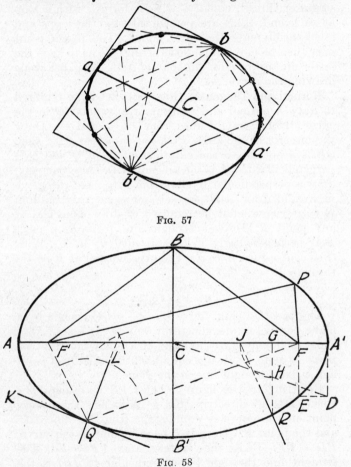

Fig. 57

Fig. 58

straight lines are together equal to AA'. Thus, in the figure, $PF + PF' = AA'$; P being any point in the curve.

The string method of constructing the curve is based upon this property, and is as follows : A piece of string or thread, equal to AA', is formed with a loop at each end. Pins are passed through the loops and stuck firmly into the focal points. The pencil point may then be moved along the string—so as to keep the latter uniformly taut—in contact with the paper while drawing the curve.

Normal and Tangents. (Fig. 58.) Let it be required to draw a normal and tangent at any point Q in the curve. Draw straight lines from Q to F and F'. Draw the bisector of the angle FQF', as shown at QL ; then QL is a normal to the elliptical curve at Q and QK, perpendicular to QL is the tangent at Q. Alternatively, draw a perpendicular to AA' from F to meet the curve in E, and draw $A'D$ parallel and equal to FE. Join D to C. Now let it be required to draw a normal at any point R. Draw a straight line from R to meet AA' perpendicularly in G, and cut DC in H. With G as centre turn H to J. Then the normal at R passes through J.

THE PARABOLA

The *parabola* (Fig. 59) is a conic section made by a plane parallel to one generator only of the cone. Also, a parabolic curve is the locus of a point moving in a plane so as to be always equidistant from a fixed point and a fixed straight line in the plane.

Referring to the figure : Let PVS be a parabolic curve, DD' its directrix, and F its focus ; then every point in the curve is equidistant from the line DD' and the point F. Thus, if P be any point in the curve, $PD = PF$. V is the vertex, and $VF = Vd$. The straight line through V perpendicular to DD is the

axis and contains the focus F. If PQ be a tangent at
any point P in the curve, and PA be perpendicular to
the axis, $VA = VQ$. Let PR be the normal at any
point P in the curve ; then AR, called the *sub-normal*,
is constant, and equal to Fd ; also $FR = FQ$. If PD

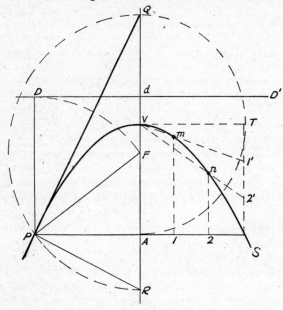

Fig. 59

be perpendicular to DD', the tangent PQ bisects the
angle DPF. Since QPR is a right angle, and $FR = FQ$,
P, R and Q are in the circumference of the circle, centre
F, radius FP.

To inscribe a parabola in a rectangle.

Let $AVTS$ be a rectangle, VA being the axis of the
required curve. Divide SA and ST into the same
number of equal parts. Draw radials from V to the

division points in TS, and draw parallels to AV from the division points in AS; then the points of intersection, m and n, are points in the curve.

THE HYPERBOLA

The *hyperbola* is a section of a right circular cone by a plane inclined at less than half the vertex angle to the axis of the cone. From this it follows that the section plane will always cut both sheets of a double cone and will, therefore, have two branches.

The curve may also be defined as the locus of a point moving in a plane, so as to have the ratio of its distances from a fixed point and a fixed straight line in the plane constant, and greater than unity.

The most useful practical properties are shown in Fig. 60, and are as follows : $Pgkjh$ is one branch of the curve, and it is symmetrical about the principal axis $V'V$ produced. Let kj and gh be any two parallel chords of the curve ; then the straight line through the mid-points q and r respectively of the chords meets the principal (or transverse) axis of the curve in C, the centre of the complete conic.

With C as centre, draw a circle through the two vertices V and V' ; then that part of any tangent contained by this circle makes a right angle with each of the straight lines drawn from its extremities to the foci. Thus, if PT is a tangent, and F and F' are the foci, the angles $EE'F'$ and $E'EF$ are right angles. Let P be the point of contact of the tangent that meets the axis in T, and let PM be perpendicular to the axis (PM is called a semi-ordinate) ; then CV is the mean proportional between CT and CM ; therefore, a circle on CM will cut the circle on VV' in T', such that TT' will be perpendicular to VV'.

With C as centre, draw a circle through the focal

points F and F'', and draw the vertex tangent to cut this circle in points A and A'; then the straight lines from C through A and A' are asymptotic to the curve.

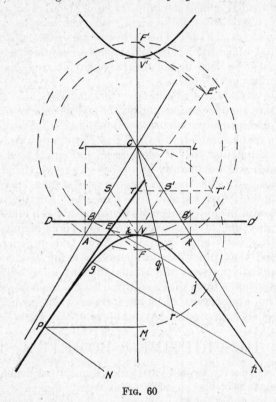

Fig. 60

The asymptotes CA and CA' are lines which continue to approach the curve but can never actually meet it, however far produced; in this particular case the asymptotes may be regarded as tangents having their points of contact with the curve at infinity.

The asymptotes may not be regarded as in any way fanciful, since they have some very practical uses and properties. Thus, all parallelograms having two adjacent sides in the asymptotes and an angular point in the curve are equal in area ; one such parallelogram is shown at $CSVS'$. This property provides a simple method of construction under certain conditions, and may also be used in the measurement of areas having irregular curved outlines.

The asymptotes also relate the curve to cone, since they are the projections, on to the section plane, of the two generators parallel to section plane. LL is a second axis of symmetry, called the conjugate axis, and is perpendicular to VV' through C and equal to AA'.

Space will not permit of a more extensive survey of the properties of the conics, but the student may, if he chooses, find a great deal more that is interesting and useful in this connection. It should be remembered that any one of the curves provides enough material to fill a very large volume, and it is not generally realized that practical problems involving the conics occasionally present the available data in so meagre and unusual a form that a solution is only made possible by the application of some property or properties previously regarded as having no practical value.

DESCRIPTIVE GEOMETRY

The capacity to deal with the geometrical problems arising out of the shaping of materials depends, in a great measure, on the capacity to reduce the material (mentally) to the condition of geometrical lines and surfaces. The faces and edges of a truly planed piece of wood may be regarded as geometric planes ; the arrises in which the surfaces intersect may be regarded as straight lines ; and the intersection of the arrises may be regarded as geometric points. The problems, then, of determining the true shapes of inclined or oblique surfaces, of finding the real angles between the required surfaces, or of finding the angles between required arrises, or between arrises and surfaces, etc., are all identical with the problems on geometrical points, lines, and planes.

The method of dealing geometrically with points and lines in space is to project them on to the plane of the paper, in accordance with one or two simple rules, and to obtain the required results by a manipulation of the projections.

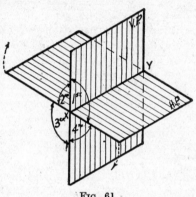

The principal planes of projection are: the "Horizontal Plane," referred to subsequently as *HP*,

FIG. 61

and the "Vertical Plane," or *VP*. If a straight line be drawn in any desired position on a sheet of paper, or other drawing surface, and the paper be then folded about the line to form a right angle, one section of the paper may be regarded as *VP*, the other as *HP*; the latter being theoretically considered as being parallel to the surface of still water.

The straight line about which the paper is bent is called the "Ground Line," or *XY*, and the surfaces of the paper must be considered as extending indefinitely in each direction. Refer to Fig. 61.

It will be seen from the figure that if *HP* and *VP* be the two sections of the paper folded to form a right angle about XY, and if VP be supposed to continue below HP and HP to continue behind VP, the two planes form four right angles. These angles are called the four dihedral angles, and are referred to as 1st, 2nd, 3rd, and 4th respectively.

Any point situated above HP and in front of VP is in the 1st dihedral angle ; a point above HP and behind VP is in the 2nd ; a point below HP and behind VP is in the 3rd ; a point below HP and in front of VP is in the 4th dihedral angle.

In arranging the given lines and points of a problem involving the planes of projection it is desirable to keep all the working in the 1st dihedral angle, but this is not always possible or convenient owing to limitations of space, or inability to foresee the extent or direction of lines developed in the process of solution. It is necessary, therefore, to consider the conditions created by lines wholly or partly in one or more of the 2nd, 3rd, or 4th dihedral angles.

Suppose the VP to remain stationary while the front section of HP moves downwards, as indicated by the arrow ; then the section of HP behind VP will move upwards as indicated, until the two planes VP and HP coincide.

The drawing surface is, therefore, always regarded as a HP and VP turned to coincide in the manner explained, and the projections of four points, one in each dihedral angle, would be as follows : 1st dihedral angle, plan below XY, elevation above XY ; in the 2nd dihedral angle, plan and elevation both above XY ; in the 3rd dihedral angle, plan above XY, elevation below XY (the reverse of the 1st) ; in the 4th dihedral angle, plan and elevation both below XY (the reverse of the 2nd).

If the plan of a point be always indicated by the small letter corresponding to the capital letter used in

reference to the actual point, and the same small letter
with a dash be used to indicate the elevation of the point,
thus, actual point *P*, plan *p*, elevation *p′*, the position
of a point in any of the four dihedral angles may be
indicated.

Since a projection of a point is always in the foot of
a perpendicular to the plane containing the projection
from the point, the
following   condition
between the two pro-
jections always exists :
*The plan and elevation
of a point are in the
same   s t r a i g h t   l i n e
perpendicular   to   the
ground line.*

Fig. 62 represents a
pictorial view cf a
figure   *ABCD*   pro-
jected on to *HP* in
abcd, and on to *VP* in
a′b′c′d′.   The   actual
projectors,   *Aa*,   *Aa′*,

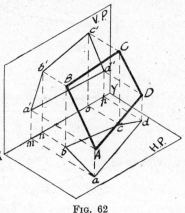

Fig. 62

Bb, *Bb′*, *Cc*, *Cc′*, *Dd* and *Dd′*, are not in either *HP*
or *VP*, and are not necessary in true projection, since
the projections of these projectors are actually in the
planes and are equal in length to the projectors
themselves. Thus, *Aa = ma′* = the height of *A* above
HP ; *Aa′ = ma* = the distance of *A* from *VP* ; and
similarly for the other points. For the sake of simpli-
city, the straight line joining the plan and elevation
of any point is called a projector, but actually the
projector is only in the drawing surface when the
point itself is in the plane, *HP* or *VP*.

The straight line in space presents the following
problems : To determine the actual length of the line ;

to determine the inclination of the line to *HP*, to *VP*, to a second line, or to a plane other than the planes of projection ; to determine the points (called " traces ") in which the line, produced if necessary, intersects the planes of projection or other plane or planes.

When a straight line is parallel to *VP* the length of

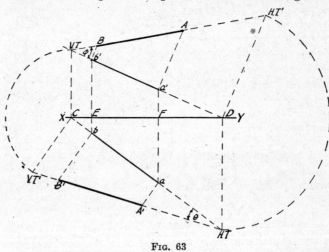

FIG. 63

its elevation is equal to the length of the actual line, and the angle between the elevation and *XY* is equal to the inclination of the line to *HP*.

When a straight line is parallel to *HP*, the length of its plan is equal to the actual length of the line, and the angle between the plan and *XY* is equal to the inclination of the line to *VP*.

When a straight line is inclined to both *HP* and *VP*, neither its true length nor its inclination to either plane of projection is shown in either plan or elevation.

Given the projections of a straight line, AB, to determine its true length, its inclinations, and its traces. (Fig. 63.)

Let ab and $a'b'$ be the given plan and elevation respectively. Draw aA' and bB' perpendicular to ab and equal to Fa' and Eb' respectively, and join A' to B'; then $A'B'$ is the true length of the line rabatted about its plan into HP.

Similarly, draw $a'A$ and $b'B$ perpendicularly to $a'b'$ and equal to Fa and Eb respectively; then AB is the true length of the line rabatted about its elevation into VP.

Produce ab to meet XY in C, and erect a perpendicular to XY from C to meet $a'b'$ produced in VT. Then VT is the vertical trace of the line and is in AB produced, and the angle between AB and $a'b'$ (ϕ) is the inclination of the line to VP.

Produce $b'a'$ to meet XY in D and draw a perpendicular to XY from D to meet ba produced in HT. Then HT is the horizontal trace of the line and is in $B'A'$ produced, and the angle between $A'B'$ and ab (θ) is the inclination of the line to HP.

Draw a perpendicular to aC from C to meet $A'B'$ produced in VT'; then C–VT' equals C–VT. Draw a perpendicular to $b'D$ from D to meet BA produced in HT'; then D–HT' equals D–HT.

Second Case. (Fig. 64.) Here the projections both approach XY towards the same side of the figure, and unless the actual line intersects XY, one or the other of the traces is in either the 2nd or 4th dihedral angle (in this case, the 4th). Again, $aA' = Ea'$, $bB' = Fb'$, $a'A = Ea$, $b'B = Fb$, HT is the horizontal trace and VT is the vertical trace. θ is the inclination to HP and ϕ is the inclination to VP. Also, AB and $A'B'$ each equal the true length of the line. It should be noted that the line, when produced, passes through HP at the point HT and meets VP in the point VT, the latter being below HP an amount equal to C–VT.

Inclined and Oblique Planes. (Fig. 65.) A pictorial

view of five planes is given in the figure. The plane (1) is inclined to *HP* and perpendicular to *VP*; (2) is inclined to *VP* and perpendicular to *HP*; (3) is inclined to both *VP* and *HP* and has parallel traces; these three types are called inclined planes. The plane (4) is an acute-angled oblique plane, and is inclined to both

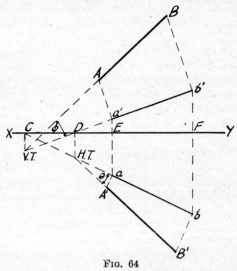

Fig. 64

HP and *VP*. (5) is an obtuse-angled oblique plane, and is inclined to both *HP* and *VP*.

Two planes always intersect in a straight line, and the lines of intersection between a plane and the planes of projection are called the vertical and horizontal traces of the plane, and are indicated by the letters " *vth.*"

The problems that arise in connection with planes are: To determine the inclinations (the angles the plane makes with the planes of projection); to determine the dihedral angle between two given planes; to

determine the real angle between the traces of a plane ;
to determine the real shape or the projections of a
figure contained by the plane ; and to determine the
sections of solids cut by inclined and oblique planes.

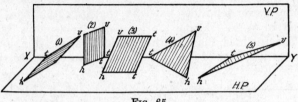

FIG. 65

Fig. 66 represents an inclined plane, similar to (1)
Fig. 65 ; *vt* is its vertical trace, *ht* is its horizontal trace,
and the angles between the traces and *XY* are the
inclinations of the plane (θ equals the inclination to

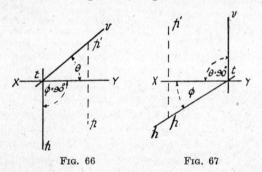

FIG. 66   FIG. 67

HP, and ϕ the inclination to *VP*). These symbols are
the Greek letters *theta* and *phi* respectively, and are
generally adopted to indicate the inclinations to the
planes of projection, thus, θ to *HP*, ϕ to *VP*. Any
point in this plane will have its elevation in *vt*, as shown
at p', and its plan in the perpendicular to *XY* from the
elevation, as at p. In Fig. 67, the plane illustrated is

similar to (2) Fig. 65, and only differs from the plane,
Fig. 66, by being reversed with respect to *VP* and *HP*.
Every point in this plane will have its plan in *HP*,
and its elevation somewhere in the perpendicular to
XY from the plan. In both planes the position of a
point is not definitely fixed by the projection that is
situated in the trace.

The Inclined Plane with Parallel Traces. (Fig. 68.)
The inclinations of this plane are not indicated by the

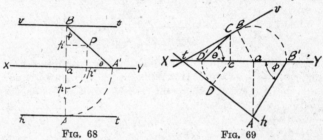

FIG. 68   FIG. 69

traces, as in the two preceding examples. Draw any
perpendicular to *XY* to cut the horizontal trace in *A*,
the vertical trace in *B*, and the ground line in *a*. With
a as centre turn *A* into *XY* at *A'* and join *A'* to *B*;
then θ and ϕ are the inclinations to *HP* and *VP*
respectively. Let *p* be the plan of any point in the
plane; then, if *p* be turned about *a* to *p''* and projected
into *A'B* at *P*, a horizontal from *P* will cut *aB* in *p'*,
the elevation of the point. (*P* is the actual point
rabatted about *aB* into *VP*.)

*To determine the inclinations of an acute-angled
oblique plane.* (Fig. 69.)

Let *vth* be the traces of the given plane. Draw any
line, *Ba*, at right angles to *vt*, and from *a* draw a perpendicular to *XY* to meet *ht* in *A*. With *a* as centre,
turn *B* into *XY* at *B'* and join *B'* to *A*; then ϕ is the
inclination of the oblique plane to *VP*.

From any point D in ht, draw a perpendicular to ht to cut XY in c. With c as centre turn D into XY at D' and join D' to C (cC is perpendicular to XY); then θ is the inclination of the oblique plane to HP.

To determine the inclinations of an obtuse-angled oblique plane. (Fig. 70.)

The traces of the given plane are at vth. The lines and points involved in this figure are lettered precisely

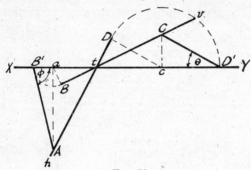

Fig. 70

as in the preceding example, and the explanation of the construction is equally applicable to both cases.

Given one projection of a point in an oblique plane, to determine the second projection. (Fig. 71.)

Let vth be the traces of the given plane and p or p' the given projection. Draw pc parallel to ht, or $p'c'$ parallel to XY. Draw cc' and pp' both perpendicular to XY; then the second projection is determined. For a horizontal line in a plane is parallel to the horizontal trace of the plane, and, because parallel lines project parallel, the *plan* of a horizontal line in a plane is parallel to the horizontal trace of the plane; then pc and $p'c'$ are the projections of a horizontal line that is in the plane and contains the point.

Second Method. Let p be the given projection. **Draw**

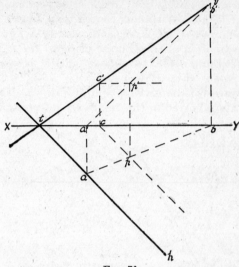

FIG. 71

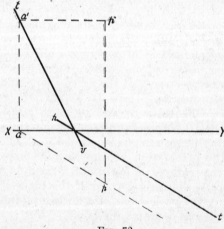

FIG. 72

any straight line through p to meet ht in a and XY in
b, and make an angle other than 90° with XY. Project
a to a' and b to b' and join a' to b'. Erect a perpendicular
to XY from p to meet $a'b'$ in p'.

If p' be given, draw $a'b'$ and project to ab, and draw
pp' as before.

When the plane is obtuse angled, as in Fig. 72, it
is only necessary to note
that p' falls above vt; ap
and $a'p'$ being the pro-
jections of a horizontal
line through the given
point, as before.

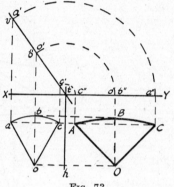

*Given the projections of
a figure lying in an in-
clined plane, to determine
the true shape of the figure.*
(Fig. 73.)

Let vth be the traces
of the given plane and
$abco$, $a'b'c'o'$ the projections of the given figure.

FIG. 73

With t as centre turn a', b', c', o' to a'', b'', c'', o'' in XY.
Draw parallels and perpendiculars to XY from a, b,
c, o and a'', b'', c'', o'' respectively, to intersect in A, B,
C and O respectively. Then $ABCO$ is the required true
shape of the figure. It should be noted that, if the true
shape were given, the projections may be obtained by
drawing the lines in the reverse order.

*Given the traces of an oblique plane, to determine :
the real angle between the traces, an edge view of the plane,
and the true shape of a figure lying in the plane by rabat-
ment into HP and VP.* (Fig. 74.)

Let vth be the traces of the given plane, abc, $a'b'c'$
the projections of a triangle contained by the plane.
Draw a straight line from v to meet XY perpendicularly

in D. Draw DV'' parallel to ht and equal Dv. Draw DE perpendicular to ht and join E to V''; then $V''E$ is an edge view of the oblique plane. Thus, if DE be regarded as a new ground line and $V''E$ as a new vertical trace, these two lines, together with ht, constitute an inclined plane similar to that in Fig. 73, and may be dealt with in the same manner. The process

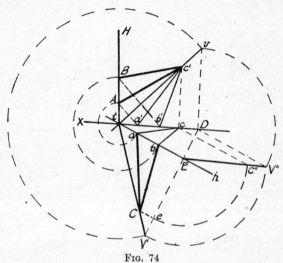

Fig. 74

may, therefore, be described as converting an oblique plane into an inclined plane.

Produce DE to V', making tV' equal to tv; then $V'th$ is the real angle between the traces of the oblique plane, and $V't$ is the vertical trace rabatted into HP. Note that EV' equals EV''.

Project c perpendicular to DE to c'' in EV'', and with E as centre turn c'' to e. Draw eC parallel to ht and join C to a and to b; then Cab is the true shape of the triangle rabatted into HP.

From b' draw a perpendicular to vt to meet a circular arc, centre t, radius tb in B, and draw a straight line from t through B. Draw $a'A$ perpendicular to vt and join A and B to c' ; then ABc' is the true shape of the

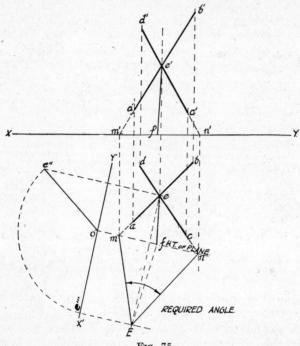

Fig. 75

triangle rabatted into VP, and tH is the horizontal trace rabatted into VP.

To determine the plane to contain two given intersecting straight lines, to determine the real angle between the lines, and to draw the projections of the bisector of the angle. (Fig. 75.)

Let ab and cd be the plans, $a'b'$ and $c'd'$ the elevations

of the given lines. Produce the elevations to meet
XY in m' and n', and project these points into the plans
(produced) to determine the horizontal traces m and n.
The straight line through m and n is the horizontal
trace of the plane containing the lines. Draw $X'Y'$
perpendicular to and intersecting mn in o. Project
e to e'', making the height of e'' above $X'Y'$ equal to the

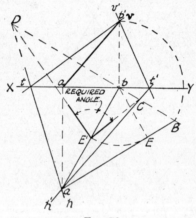

Fig. 76

height of e' above XY, and with o as centre turn e'' to
e'''. Draw a perpendicular to mn from e to intersect
a perpendicular to $X'Y'$ from e''' in E. Draw Em and
En ; then nEm is the required angle between the lines.
Draw the bisector of the angle nEm to intersect mn
in f and project f to f' ; then fe and $f'e'$ are the projections of the bisector of the angle between the lines.

*To determine the dihedral angle between two given
planes.* (Fig. 76.)

The angle between two intersecting planes is the
angle between two straight lines, one in each plane,
each line perpendicular to the line of intersection

between the planes. Let *vth* and *v't'h'* be the traces of
the given planes, and let *a* and *b'* be the intersections
of the horizontal and vertical traces respectively.

Project *a* into *XY* at *a'* and *b'* into *XY* at *b*, and
draw *ab* and *a'b'* ; then *ab* and *a'b'* are the projections
of the line of intersection between the given planes.
Draw a perpendicular to *ab*, through *b*, to meet *h't'* in

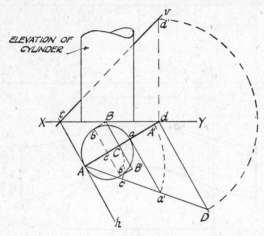

ELEVATION OF
CYLINDER

FIG. 77

C and *ht* produced in *D*. Produce *bC* to *B*, making
bB equal to *bb'* and join *B* to *a*. Draw *bE* perpendicular
Ba, and with *b* as centre, *bE* as radius, cut *ba* in *E'*.
Draw *E'C* and *E'D* ; then *DE'C* is the required dihedral
angle.

*To determine the axes of the elliptic section of a right
cylinder made by an oblique cutting plane.* (Fig. 77.)

The circle, centre *c*, is the plan of the cylinder, *vth*
the traces of the given plane. Draw *Ad* through *c* and
perpendicular to *ht*, and draw *dd'* at right angles to
XY. Draw *dD* perpendicular to *Ad* and equal to *dd'*,

and join D to A. Draw bb' parallel to ht through c, and produce to cut AD in c'. Draw a parallel to ht from a to meet AD in a'. Turn c' and a' about A to C and A' respectively, and draw CB and CB' parallel and equal to cb and cb' respectively. Then AA' and BB' are the required axes.

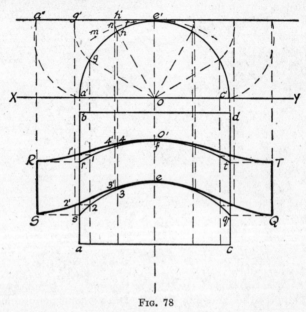

Fig. 78

To develop any required section of the surface of a right cylinder. (Fig. 78.)

Let the semicircle $a'e'c'$, centre o, be the end elevation of the cylindrical surface, and let $rftqes$ be the plan of the section of the surface required to be developed.

Divide the elevation curve into any number of equal parts, as $a'g$, gh, he', and draw perpendiculars to XY from g, h, and e' to cut the arcs sq and rt in points

1, 2, 3, 4, *f* and *e*. Produce *e′o* to *o′*, making *oo′* equal to half *oe′* and with *o′* as centre, *o′c′* as radius, draw the arc *mnpe′*, making the distances *ma′*, *me′* equal ; *ng*, *ne′* equal ; *ph*, *pe′* equal. Draw *a″e′* parallel to *XY*, and with *m* as centre turn *a′* to *a″*, *n* as centre turn *g*

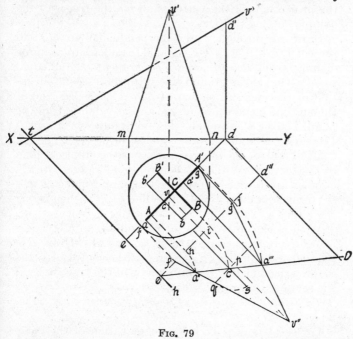

FIG. 79

to *g′*, and with *p* as centre turn *h* to *h′*. Deal with the second quadrant in a similar way. Draw parallels to *XY* from *r* and *s* to intersect a perpendicular to *XY* from *a″* in *R* and *S* respectively. Draw perpendiculars to *XY* from *g′* and *h′*, and parallels to *XY* from 1, 2, 3, and 4, to obtain the points 1′, 2′, 3′, and 4′. Draw smooth curves through *S*, 2′, 3′, *e* and through *R*, 1′, 4′, and *f*. Repeat on the other side of the centre line to obtain the required development, *RSQT*.

To obtain the elliptic section of a right cone made by an oblique cutting plane. (Fig. 79.)

The triangle *mv'n* is the elevation of the cone, *v*, *v'* the projections of the vertex, and *vth* the traces of the oblique cutting plane.

Draw *ed* through *v* and perpendicular to *ht*, and project *d* to *d'*. Draw *e'd''* parallel to and at any suitable distance from *ed*, and make *d''D* parallel to *ht* and equal to *dd'*. On *e'd''* as ground line, project a second elevation of the cone, as shown at *f'g'v''*. Draw *De'* to cut the outline generators in *a''* and *a'''*, and draw *pq* parallel to *e'd''* through the mid-point *c'* of *a''a'''*. Project *a''*, *c'* and *a'''* to *a*, *c* and *a'* respectively; then *c* is the centre, *aa'* the major axis of the elliptical plan of the section. With *p* as centre, *pq* as radius, draw a circular arc to cut *cc'* produced in *s*, and make *cb* and *cb'* each equal to *c's* and parallel to *ht*; then *bb'* is the minor axis of elliptical plan of the section.

With *e'* as centre, turn *a''*, *c'*, and *a'''* to *h*, *i*, and *j* respectively, and project to *A*, *C*, and *A'*. Draw *BB'* parallel and equal to *bb'*; then *C* is the centre, *AA'* the major axis, and *BB'* the minor axis of the true shape of the section.

To develop the surface of a right circular cone. (Fig. 80.)

Let the triangle *ABV* be the elevation of the cone. Draw the semicircle on *AB* and divide it into any number of equal parts, numbering the points of division as shown; there are six equal divisions in the example given. With *V* as centre, *VB* as radius, draw the arc *BB'* equal to twice the length of the semicircle; twelve divisions, each equal to one plan division, stepped along the arc *BB'*, will give a very close approximation of the required length.

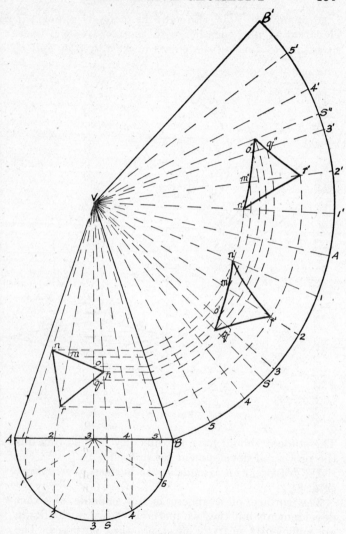

Fig. 80

A triangular hole through the cone is shown in elevation at *npr*, together with the construction lines necessary to develop the points in *m*, *n*, *o*, *p*, *q*, and *r*.

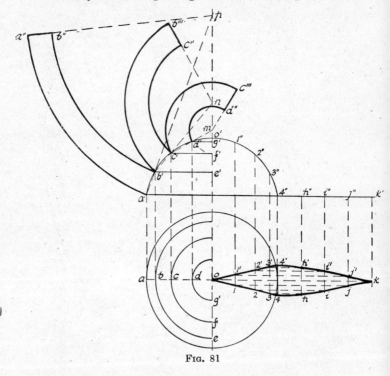

FIG. 81

The student should have no difficulty in following out the process of development for himself.

To develop, approximately, the surface of a sphere. (Fig. 81.)

The surface of a sphere is not capable of exact development, but the two methods shown in the figure are sufficiently near for most practical purposes. The circle, centre o, is the plan, the arc $a'o'4''$ the elevation, of a section of a sphere. The half of the surface to the left of the centre line is developed in "zones," and on the right of the centre line the method of developing the surface in "lunes" is shown.

The plan semicircles a, b, c, and d, are the boundary lines of the three zones selected for development. Each zone is regarded as being part of the surface of a right cone, and the process of development is then as follows : Consider the part of the surface lying between the plan semicircles b and c ; the elevations of the semicircles being the horizontal lines $b'e'$ and $c'f'$. Draw a straight line through the points b' and c' to meet the centre line produced in n. With n as centre, radii nc' and nb', draw the circular arcs $c'c''$ and $b'b'''$ making the length of the arc $c'c''$ equal to the plan semicircle c, and draw the radial line $nc''b'''$; then the area $b'b'''c''c'$ is the required development.

The remaining zones are developed in a similar manner ; the length of the arc $b'b''$ being equal to that of the arc $b'b'''$, and the arc $c'c'''$ equal to the arc $c'c''$. It should be noted that only half of the surface of the section of the sphere is developed.

Refer to the surface on the right of the centre line : The plan sector between the radials 04 and $04'$ represents the plan of one lune, and since all equal lunes of the same sphere are precisely the same in development, only one requires to be considered. Divide the elevation quadrant $0'4''$ into any number of parts (equal parts for convenience), as shown at $0'1''$, $1''-2''$, $2''-3''$, $3''-4''$, and set these parts off along $a'4''$ produced, as at $4''h''$, $h''i''$, $i''j''$, and $j''k'$. Project $1''$, $2''$, $3''$, and $4''$ to $1-1'$, $2-2'$, $3-3'$, and $4-4'$ respectively, and by drawing parallels to $a'k'$ from the points in plan to meet perpendiculars to $a'k'$ from h'', i'', j'', and k', obtain the development $4k4'$, as shown.

It will, of course, be understood that as a spherical surface has curvature in three dimensions, no method can be found for developing it exactly on a two dimensional surface, i.e. a plane surface. However, the method described above can be used to obtain a very close approximation, by dividing the surface into a sufficiently large number of zones.

SECTION VII

WINDOWS

BY

T. CORKHILL, F.B.I.C.C., M.I.Struct.E.

SECTION VII

WINDOWS

WINDOWS are glazed frames primarily intended for the admission of light ; but ornamentation and ventilation are also important considerations. The construction aims at providing these features, with protection against the weather and with sufficient strength to withstand usage.

The area of the glass, for habitable rooms, must be at least one-tenth of the floor area, and at least half of that area must open. The top of the opening parts must be 6 ft. 3 in. to 7 ft. above the floor according to the position of the room.

A window usually consists of a frame and sashes. The frame is that part of the woodwork which is fixed to the wall and which carries the sash, while the sash carries the glass. The frames are broadly divided into two classes, known as *cased* or *boxed* frames, and *solid* frames.

Classification. The ordinary types of windows may be classified as follows: Fast sheets, sliding sashes, pivoted sashes, casement windows, and Yorkshire lights. There are many variations of the sliding sashes and of the casement windows.

Dimensions. The sizes of the opening in the brickwork are used to denote the size of a window, irrespective of the amount of the frame buried in the jambs.

Fast Sheets. A window that has no frame, and consists of a sash only, is called a *fast sheet*, *stand sheet*, or *fixed sash*. The usual kind is shown in Fig. 1. It is used for workshops, for inside walls, and for unimportant positions generally, where ventilation can be provided by other means.

The fast, or stand, sheet usually consists of two stiles, bottom rail, top rail, and intermediate bars if required.

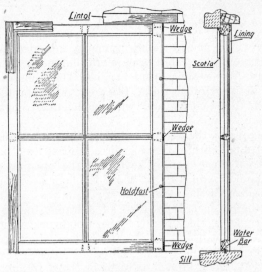

FIG. 1. STAND SHEET WINDOW

The bars may be for ornamentation, but usually they are intended to give a smaller square, or pane, of glass. This is an important consideration in factories where breakages are common.

" Sash Stuff." The usual material for making sashes is redwood, and it is known as "sash stuff." It is stocked by most builders and timber merchants. The sizes are 2 in. by 2 in., and 3 in. by 2 in., while the bars are 2 in. by 1 in. or $1\frac{1}{4}$ in. The finished sizes are $\frac{1}{8}$ in. less in every case. Fig. 2 shows the usual section.

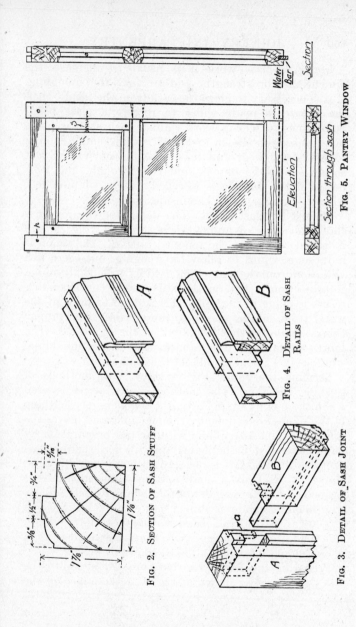

Water
Bar

Section

Elevation

Section through sash

FIG. 5. PANTRY WINDOW

A

B

FIG. 4. DETAIL OF SASH RAILS

5/8"
3/4"
3/8" 1/2"
1/8"
1/8"
1/8"

FIG. 2. SECTION OF SASH STUFF

B

a

A

FIG. 3. DETAIL OF SASH JOINT

For good-class work it is usual to increase the dimensions for strength, and to vary the moulding. If it is necessary to glaze the sash from the inside, then the rebate is made wider to receive a glass bead. Sometimes for cheap work thinner sash stuff is used, but the section shown in Fig. 2 is quite small enough to withstand wear and tear. The bottom rail of fast sheets should be of oak and run through, and it is better if the outside is bevelled instead of moulded, when the glazing is on the inside.

Details for Fast Sheet. The detail for the joints is shown in Figs. 3 and 4. The stiles *A*, Fig. 3, are mortised to receive the tenoned rails *B*. The tenon is reduced in width to allow for wedging, but there is a variation from the haunching used for panelled framing. A projection is left on the stile and a corresponding recess is made in the rail. This is done to prevent the water from gaining access to the mortise. The projection is made on the " square " of the moulding. The mortise is also on the square part of the moulding, whether it is in the middle of the stuff or not.

Scribing the Joint. Fig. 4 shows two methods of scribing the rails. The method shown at *A* is used when the tenons are made on the tenoner ; the scribing of the moulding is done by the machine, and leaves the joint ready for assembling without any preparation by hand, except for the haunching. When the joint is prepared by hand, it is usual to scribe the moulding, as shown at *B*. Only a small portion of the moulding is scribed and the remainder of the shoulder is left square. The machine-made scribing is shown by full lines in Fig. 3, and the hand-made scribing by dotted lines. For the latter it is necessary to remove a small portion of the moulding on the stile, as shown at *a*.

Preparing the Bars. The bars are tenoned into the stiles and rails, as shown in Fig. 1, and wedged in the usual way. Occasionally, stub tenons are used where the stiles or rails are short, and stiff enough to withstand bending. The intersections of the bars are the same as explained for the sash doors. (See Fig. 32 in " Doors and Frames.")

Pantry Window. This is an extension of the stand sheet, used where ventilation has to be provided. It has a small sash arranged, or inset, in the larger sash, to provide the ventilation, as shown in Fig. 5. The small sash is often called a **type sash,** because it is of the same type as the surrounding sash, and made from the same kind of stuff. The small sash may be hinged, but it is usually pivoted.

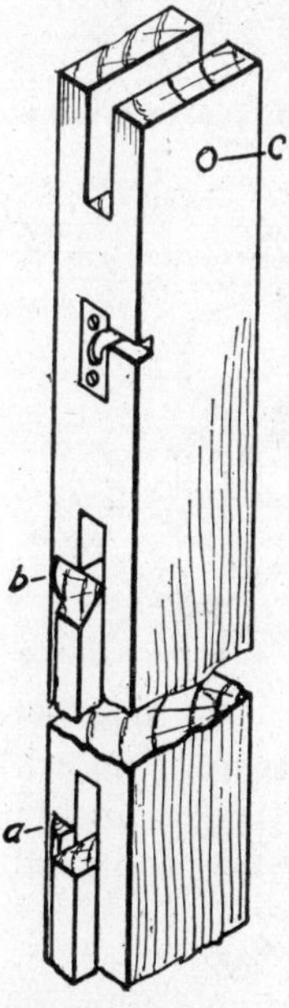

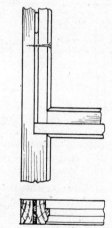

FIG. 6. PREPARING STILE

FIG. 7. REBATING SASH

Preparing the Stiles. The moulding is removed on the stiles above the transom, as shown in Fig. 6. The joint between the transom and stile is an ordinary mortise and tenon, and it is usually scribed, as shown at *a*. The moulding is sometimes mitred, as shown at *b*, especially for intricate mouldings that do not lend themselves to scribing, rather than to the ovolo shown in the illustration.

Often the stile is reduced beyond the moulding, so as to make the *glass lines* for the type sash and the

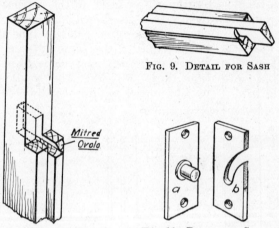

FIG. 9. DETAIL FOR SASH

Mitred
Ovolo

FIG. 8. REDUCED STILE   FIG. 10. PIVOT AND SOCKET

sheet more uniform, as shown in Fig. 7. The method of preparing the stile to receive the transom is shown in Fig. 8. This method strengthens the transom considerably ; but it entails more labour and also reduces the effective lighting area because the sheet must have a bigger *margin* to allow the sash to open.

The Head is usually prepared with an open mortise and tenon joint, and fixed by pins *c*, Fig. 6. This allows for adjusting the head *after* the sash is pivoted, and eases the fitting considerably. The head and transom are rebated for the sash, as shown in the end view, Fig. 5.

The Sash Joints are made in the same way as those for the sheet. Usually, the stuff is too narrow to receive a haunching, and the joints are pinned instead of being wedged. For good work it is usual to make a dovetailed joint. The detail for the rails when they are dovetailed is shown in Fig. 9.

The top and bottom rails of the sash are rebated, but the stiles are square on the edges. When the stiles are rebated the pivoting is more complicated. It is easier to hinge the sash either to the head or to the

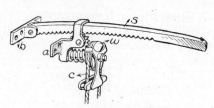

Fig. 11. Turn Button   Fig. 12. Quadrant

transom when the sides are rebated, as explained for casement windows.

Pivoting the Sash. The sash may be hung on pivots, or it may be hung on two strong screws. The screws make a satisfactory cheap job, but pivots are used in good work. The usual type of stud or pivot a, and socket b, is shown in Fig. 10, and the method of fixing the socket to the stile of the sheet is shown in Fig. 6. The pivots are *let in* and screwed to the sash stile, and then they are dropped into the slots in the stiles of the sheet leading to the sockets. Alternative methods and more difficult examples of pivoting will be shown later.

Pivots may be obtained to screw on to the face of the sash. They are much easier to fix, but more consideration has to be given to the bevels for the top and bottom rebates, as explained for " Shutting Joints."

Opening and Closing Sash. It is advisable to place the pivots or screws a little above the centre of the height, so that the sash will keep closed by its own weight. A *turn button*, Fig. 11, is used to secure the sash when it is closed.

A cord is used to regulate the opening of the sash. It is fixed to two small screw eyes, one at the top and one at the bottom of the sash. When the sash is hung by hinges it is usual to use a quadrant for regulating the opening of the sash.

A Quadrant, or fanlight opener, with an endless cord, is shown in Fig. 12. Simpler types may be obtained, but

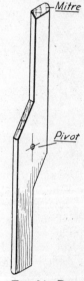

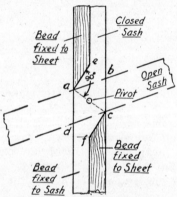

FIG. 13. CUTTING THE BEADS

FIG. 14. BEAD FOR SASH

the example shown is generally used for good work. The plate *a* is fixed to the sash and the plate *b* to the frame. When the endless cord *c* is moved it revolves the pulley *w*, which in turn moves the sprocketed wheel along the stay *s*. The plate *a* moves with the mechanism, and so opens or closes the sash.

Rebated Sashes increase the labour considerably, but they are preferred because the closed joint excludes draughts and dust. The difficulty lies in preparing the beads for the rebates on the stiles. It is much easier to *plant* the rebates than to prepare them on the solid, and usually they are prepared as shown in Figs. 7 and 13. The planted beads are usually about $\frac{5}{16}$ in. thick.

Preparing the Beads. The method of cutting the rebates is shown in Fig. 13. The end view of the sash is drawn in two positions, when the sash is closed and also when the sash is open at the maximum required position. The sash should not be quite level when it is opened, so that it can throw off the rain.

The intersection of the two outlines gives a rhombus, as shown at *abcd*. When the shortest diagonal of the rhombus is drawn, as shown by the dotted line *ac*, then lines at right angles (*ae* and *cf*) will give the required cuts for the beads.

The shaded, or grained, portions in Fig. 13 show the parts of the bead which are fixed to the sheet, and Fig. 14 shows the part which is fixed to the sash. The rebate on the top rail of the sash is also planted and mitred with the bead fixed to the sash stiles, as shown in Fig. 14. When the pivots are screwed on to the face of the sash, the procedure is the same ; but the position of the sash when it is open must be found by rotating the sash about the pivot centre on the face of the sash, instead of at the centre of its thickness.

Wedging Up. The sheet is *wedged up* at the transom and bottom rail, after all the joints have been painted. Pins are generally used to strengthen the joints, because paint does not hold like glue. For interior work, glue would be used instead of paint. Nails are sometimes used for inferior work instead of pins. The head is left loose until the sash is completed, fitted, and hung.

It is then regulated to give clearance to the sash, and pinned, as shown at *p* in Fig. 5.

Fixing. It is usual to fix fast sheets in the reveals by wedges. They are placed at the ends of the rails, and also at the top of the stiles, unless the stiles are tight to the wood lintol, when they can be fixed by nails.

Sometimes folding wedges are used, especially where there is considerable space between the sheet and the brickwork. For large windows the wedges are supplemented by holdfasts, as shown in Fig. 1.

Water Bar. A groove is made in the bottom rail, and a corresponding groove in the stone sill, to receive a *water bar*. This is a copper, galvanized iron, or hardwood slip which is inserted in the grooves and bedded in a mixture of white lead and oil, as shown in Fig. 1. This makes the joint between the bottom rail and the stone or brick sill watertight. Oak is generally used for the slip because of its cheapness, and it is quite satisfactory for ordinary purposes. The sheet should be bedded against the brickwork in the same way as explained for external door frames.

Linings are scribed to the brick jambs and fixed to the sheet on the inside. They are also called *margins* or *facings*. They cover the space between the sheet and the brickwork, and also the wedges and holdfasts. (See Fig. 1.) When scribing the margins to the brickwork, it is best to nail lightly the margins to the sheet, so that they are parallel to the glass rebates. They look unsightly if they are not parallel to the *glass line*. The margins may be chamfered or moulded. Scotias are often mitred round the stiles and head on the outside, as shown in Fig. 1.

Factory Windows. These are large windows very similar to fast sheets, but they have one or more *type* sashes for ventilation. The stuff is about $2\frac{1}{2}$ in. or 3 in. thick, according to the size of the window, and it is chamfered instead of moulded. If the windows are accessible they are glazed with putty on the outside. But usually many of the windows are not in a convenient position to glaze them on the outside. In this case all the windows are glazed on the inside for uniformity. Beads are used for inside glazing. The usual

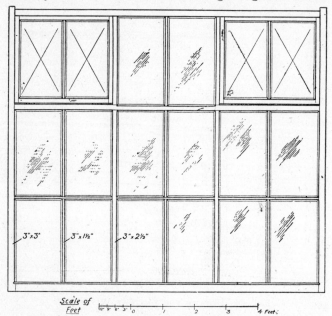

Scale of Feet

FIG. 15. FACTORY WINDOW

type of factory window is shown in Fig. 15. The crosses or diagonals on the glass denote the amount of the window arranged to open. For narrower windows the opening sash is often arranged the full width of the sheet.

Fig. 16 shows a vertical section through the centre of the sheet, and a vertical section through the sash. The horizontal members should be bevelled on the top edge to throw off the water ; all the other members are chamfered. The bead on the bottom rail is known as a *condensation* or *moisture* bead. It is hollowed out to collect the condensation from the glass, and provided with weep holes to allow the water to drain outside.

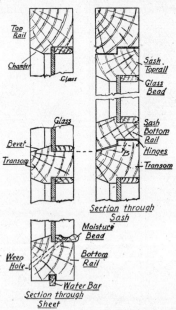

FIG. 16. DETAILS FOR FACTORY WINDOW

Details for Sashes. The transom requires the most consideration, because of the arrangement for the type sashes. These are hung at the bottom by ordinary butt hinges and opened by quadrants. The details in Fig. 16 show a continuous line on the outside for the bevel and the rebate on the transom. This is the usual method ; but it produces a broken line on the inside between the glass bead and the bead receiving the hinges. Sometimes the bead *B* for the hinges is planted so that the transom can be cut from thinner stuff. The sashes are rebated on the outside for the stiles and head, but on the inside for the bottom rail.

The head also has different details in a case where it receives the sashes. The chamfer is stopped at the sash

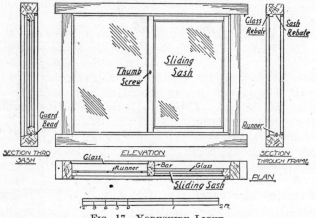

FIG. 17. YORKSHIRE LIGHT

rebates, and then the ends of the head are beaded. The bead breaks the joint between the head and the sash and continues the *chamfer line*.

SLIDING SASHES WITH SOLID FRAMES

Yorkshire Lights are windows in which one-half is arranged as a sliding sash. This arrangement requires a solid frame in which the sash can slide, and which also receives the remainder of the glass. The usual type of Yorkshire light is shown in Fig. 17.

The Frame consists of two stiles, head, and sill. The material is usually redwood with an oak sill, and it is about 5 in. by 3 in. in section. A vertical 2 in. by 2 in. bar is placed at the centre of the frame to receive the glass in the fixed part. It is usual to allow the head and sill to run through and to tenon the stiles into them.

The head is rebated on the inside for the sash, and on the outside for the glass where the glass is fixed in the frame. A plough groove is made in the sill to receive a metal or hardwood runner for the sash.

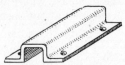

FIG. 18. METAL SHOE

One stile is rebated for the glass, while the other is chamfered or moulded. The sill should also be ploughed for a water bar, if it is for an outside wall. The plough groove should be near to the front edge of the sill. This is a better security against the water entering under the sill than when the groove is in the middle.

A Guard Bead, which is also called a *staff*, *guide*, or *inner bead*, is mitred round the inside of the frame to *guide* the sash. The usual dimensions of a guard bead are $\frac{7}{8}$ in. by $\frac{5}{8}$ in. finish.

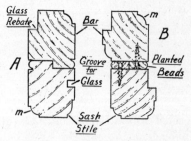

FIG. 19. DETAILS FOR MEETING STILES

The Sash is made as previously explained. The bottom rail is ploughed for the runner and throated at the front edge to throw off the water. It is usual to screw metal *shoes*, Fig. 18, on the bottom edge to engage with the runner. This prevents wear and produces smoother running of the sash.

When the frame is too narrow to receive a guard or staff bead, the sash is held in position by another runner screwed to the head of the frame. The top runner is placed in the groove in the top rail of the sash and put into position at the same time as the sash. There is no groove in the head of the frame to receive the runner, otherwise it would be impossible to place it into position.

The Runners should be of brass or hardwood, and they should be screwed securely to the frame. Iron quickly corrodes, and prevents the smooth running of the sash; this also applies to the shoes which slide on the metal runner. When it is convenient, and especially for sliding sashes inside a building, the sash is fitted with ball-bearing rollers. A flat strip of metal is screwed to the sill for the rollers to run along. Pulleys may also be obtained, consisting of a number of revolving steel balls which run along a metal runner, as shown in Fig. 17.

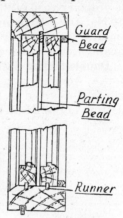

FIG. 20. VERTICAL SECTION THROUGH SLIDING SASHES

Meeting Stiles. Alternative details, where the stile of the sash and the bar meet, are shown in Fig. 19. The detail *A* is used for good

FIG. 21. HORIZONTAL SECTION THROUGH SLIDING SASHES

work. The sash stile has a plough groove to receive the glass. Solid rebates are formed on the two members, and beads are stuck on the solid to break the joints.

A detail used for cheaper work is shown at *B*. The meeting rebates are formed by planted beads, which should be of hardwood securely screwed to the stile and bar. The advantage of detail *B* is that the material is ordinary sash stuff, with an ovolo moulding formed at *m*. Any other convenient method of relieving the sharp corner may be used, such as a chamfer or a rounded corner.

Double Sliding Sashes. The vertical section for a window with two sashes sliding horizontally is given in Fig. 20, and a horizontal section in Fig. 21. The details are very similar

FIG. 22. THUMB SCREW

to those for the Yorkshire light, but all the glass is carried by the sashes. This type of window is only suitable where it is protected from the weather, because of the difficulty of keeping the level sill free from water.

A Parting Bead is used to separate the two sashes. This is a thin bead, about 1 in. by $\frac{3}{8}$ in. finish, which is inserted in plough grooves in the stiles and head.

FIG. 23
FLUSH
BOLT

A Thumb Screw is generally used for fastening the sliding sash when it is closed, as shown in Fig. 17. The usual type of thumb screw is shown in Fig. 22. The plate *b* is *let in* and screwed to the face of the bar or the back sheet, while the screw *s* passes through the stile of the front meeting stile and engages with the plate *b*.

An alternative fastening for the Yorkshire light is to use *flush bolts* on the edge of the meeting stile, so that they *shoot* into the sill and head respectively. Flush bolts are often used as an additional security to the thumb screw for double sliding sashes. An illustration of a flush bolt is given in Fig. 23.

SLIDING SASHES WITH BOX FRAMES

" Sash and Frame " Windows. When the sashes slide vertically it is necessary to balance them by weights, or to grip them by spring clips. This type of window is called a *sash and frame,* or *balanced,* or *double-hung, sashes.* It consists of a pair of sliding sashes and a boxed, or cased, frame. The window is a common type ; but at the present time it is out of favour owing to the preference for casement windows. From past experience, however, one can assume that the sash and frame will again become popular. It is more draught-proof than casements, and less liable to injury through sudden storms. The ventilation of a room can be regulated to any required amount, both at the top and bottom, thus allowing for the natural movement of the air. It is very easy to manipulate when the cords are in condition, and if a cord should be broken it does not throw the window out of action, whereas a broken hinge makes a casement window useless for ventilation. Another advantage is that it moves in its own plane ; hence, it does not disturb the window furnishings.

Fig. 24 gives several different views of the ordinary type of sash and frame. The general principles of construction are the same in all cases, but the details vary considerably according to the quality of the work. The illustration shows inside elevation, and vertical and horizontal sections. The inside linings have been removed in the inside elevation, seen in Fig. 24, to show

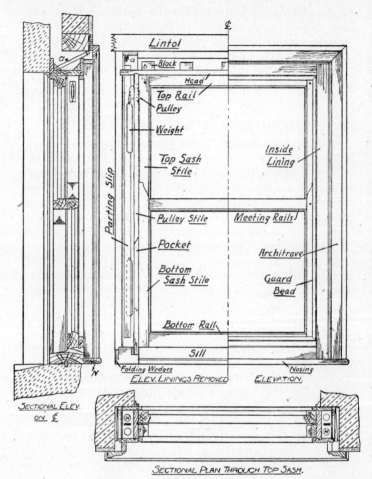

FIG. 24. SASH AND FRAME WINDOW

Lintol

Block

Head

Top Rail

Pulley

Weight

Inside Lining

Top Sash Stile

Parting Slip

Pulley Stile

Meeting Rails

Pocket

Architrave

Bottom Sash Stile

Guard Bead

Bottom Rail

Sill

Folding Wedges

Nosing

ELEV. LININGS REMOVED

ELEVATION.

SECTIONAL ELEV. ON ℄

SECTIONAL PLAN THROUGH TOP SASH.

the construction of the boxed frame. A little of the brickwork has been included to show the method of fixing and finishing the frame.

An isometric view of the different parts is given in Fig. 25. The drawings show the top and bottom corners and a portion at the centre, including the meeting rails. The distribution of the different members

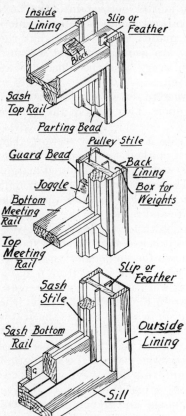

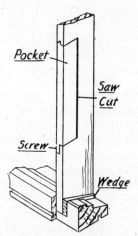

FIG. 25. DETAILS OF SASH AND
FRAME WINDOW

FIG. 26. DETAILS FOR
SILL AND STILE

is shown, and the method of forming the box for the weights.

The Frame consists of *sill, head, stiles, inner and outer*

linings, parting and *inner beads*. A rough parting *slip*,
or feather, is used to separate the weights, and a rough
back lining to prevent mortar getting into the box.
The dimensions of the various members vary considerably, according to the quality of the work, but the
dimensions given below are usually adopted, because
they are *stock sizes*. In every case the finished sizes
are $\frac{1}{8}$ in. below those given.

Setting Out. The method of setting out for a window
is similar to that for a door. Two sides of the rod are
used, as shown in Fig. 27, one side showing a vertical
section and the other side a horizontal section. The
brickwork opening is first marked, and then the various
members are arranged so as to give the required margin
round the opening. The sections of the different
members are only shown once. For instance, the double
lines at *a* show the square and rebate for the sash stuff,
which has already been shown for the head in the vertical section ; sometimes it is necessary to show special
details separately, as shown for the joggle.

The Sill, which should be of oak, is cut from 6 in. by
3 in. stuff. In good-class work it has a double rebate,
with throatings, as shown in Figs. 25 and 34 ; and it is
ploughed for the nosing, or window board, the water
bar, and for the *ventilation bead* when one is used. For
inferior work only one rebate is used, as shown in Fig.
24, and a guard bead takes the place of the ventilation
bead ; hence, no plough groove is necessary for the bead.

The ends of the sill are reduced in width to receive
the inside and outside linings, and trenched to receive
the pulley stiles, as shown in Fig. 26. Usually, the
trench is made large enough to receive a wedge to
assist in fixing the pulley stile. The ends are prepared
on the tenoner when machines are available. The
trenches are made with a special saw on the tenoner.
When wedge room is required it is necessary to run

them under the saw twice, but the second time the table fence is canted to give the required bevel for the wedge. The depth of the trench depends upon the thickness of the sill and the bevels on the top surface. The usual section of sill has about 1 in. of material left after it is trenched.

The Pulley Stiles are from 1 in. to $1\frac{1}{4}$ in. thick, according to the quality of the work and the size of the frames. The width is $4\frac{1}{2}$ in. for 2 in. sashes, without the tongues. They are cut square at the ends to the required length, which is taken from the rod. They are

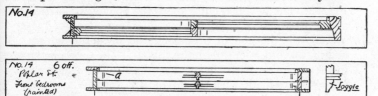

FIG. 27. ROD FOR SASH AND FRAME WINDOW

trenched into the head about $\frac{1}{4}$ in., and into the sill about $\frac{1}{4}$ in. below the lowest point of the top bevelled surface. A pulley stile prepared for the pulleys is shown in Fig. 28. Usually the edges of the stiles are left square, but in good work they are tongued, as shown in Figs. 25 and 29.

Pockets are prepared so that the weights can be removed from the boxes when it is required to hang the sashes. There is considerable variation in the preparation of the pockets, according to the quality of the work. Two methods are shown in Figs. 26 and 28. For very cheap work both ends of the pocket are prepared with one saw cut, as shown at a in Fig. 28. The pocket is then fixed in position by two screws. This method is not satisfactory, especially after the pocket has been removed several times.

A very common, and satisfactory, method is shown in Fig. 28. A single saw cut is made with the dovetail saw at *a*; and as far as possible another one is made at *b*. The cut at *c* is made with a pocket, or sash, chisel, and the saw cut *b* is completed with the pocket chisel.

The pocket is cut lengthways by *dropping* the stile, from the back, on to the circular saw, as shown in Fig. 26. When all the cuts have been made the pocket is *tapped* with the hammer until it falls away from the stile. It is then refitted and a screw is inserted at *a*, Fig. 28. The bevelled cut *c* keeps the pocket in position at the bottom.

A better method of preparing the pocket is shown in Fig. 26, but it entails more labour. The cuts on the front are made with the pocket chisel, while those on the back are made with the dovetail saw and completed with the chisel. A screw at the bottom fixes the pocket after it has been refitted. When using the pocket chisel it is usual to wet the cutting edge. This swells the fibres and closes up the cut.

Centre Pockets are often used for good work. The chief advantage of this pocket is that it allows for a continuous fixing for the inside lining on the edge of the pulley stile. The end cuts may be prepared as in Fig. 26. The vertical cuts are made by dropping the stile on to the circular saw, so that the saw cuts through to within about $\frac{3}{16}$ in. of the face. The vertical cuts are then completed from the face by a cutting gauge. In superior work, however, new pockets are prepared, so that it does not matter how the stuff is removed. The parting bead assists in keeping a centre pocket in position ; but it should be fixed by a screw, under the bottom sash, as shown in Fig. 29.

The chief disadvantage of a centre pocket is the exposure of the vertical cut *a*, so that when it is removed

it disfigures the paint. Sometimes the cut *a* is slightly
veed to prevent damaging the paint.

There are many other ways of preparing the pockets.
Every joiner thinks his own method the best; but
most firms have one particular method which they
adopt in all cases, unless the architectural details

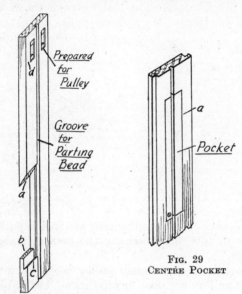

FIG. 28. PULLEY STILE
WITH POCKET REMOVED

FIG. 29
CENTRE POCKET

specify the type of pocket required. The length of the
pocket varies with the length of the weights. Usually
they are 14 in. to 16 in. long for cottage windows
They must be long enough to give free access to the
weights.

The Pulleys are let into the stiles, so that the plate
is flush with the stile. The mortises for the pulleys are

prepared on the mortising machine, but sometimes they are prepared by brace and bit. When they are mortised on the machine, it is usual to nail lightly several stiles together, so that the mortising for several stiles can be done at one operation.

Care is required for finding the position of the pulleys. They must be placed at the centre of the thickness of the sash. Hence, the outside pulley is in the middle

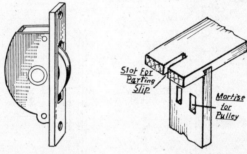

Slot for Parting Slip

Mortise for Pulley

FIG. 30. AXLE PULLEY   FIG. 31. PREPARING HEAD

of the space for the pulley, but the inside pulley is not in the middle, as shown by the greater margin at d, Fig. 28.

The usual type of sash pulley is shown in Fig. 30. Cheap pulleys are dear at any price. They are difficult to replace, as it necessitates rehanging the sash ; also there is very little material for holding the screws and the positions of the screw holes vary, so that it is often difficult to secure a second pulley. For these reasons alone it is better to have a pulley that will not corrode easily. Cheap iron pulleys often cut the cords. The pulleys are usually fixed by two screws ; some of the better qualities have four screws.

The pulley is let into the stile about 2 in. to 3 in. from the top, so that the head can be nailed to the stiles without the nails coming in contact with the pulleys.

The Head requires no preparation beyond the trenchings. Usually it is ploughed for a parting bead ; but in cheap work this is dispensed with, especially in the south. A top parting bead, as shown in Fig. 25, is invariably used in the north of England, because of the more inclement weather. The trenching is shown in Fig. 24. The section of the head is usually the same as that for the pulley stiles. If it has square edges, it is of $4\frac{1}{2}$ in. by 1 in. stuff. The width is equal to twice the thickness of the sashes plus the parting bead plus $\frac{1}{4}$ in. under the guard bead. The head projects over the stiles at the ends sufficiently to provide fixing for the linings, and for wedging the frame in the opening if required. It is the same length as the sill. The ends are slotted by means of a drunken saw, so that the parting slips can be inserted, as shown in Figs. 24 and 31. In good work the stile is often dovetailed into the head, as shown in Fig. 31, and the thickness of the head is increased to $1\frac{1}{4}$ in. or $1\frac{1}{2}$ in.

The Inside Linings are usually 3 in. by $\frac{3}{4}$ in. or $\frac{7}{8}$ in., but the width varies according to the size of the weights. When they are ploughed for the back linings they are $\frac{1}{2}$ in. wider. They are nailed to the sill, pulley stiles, and head. They should be ploughed to receive a tongue on the pulley stile and also for the jamb linings, as shown in Fig. 24. The top lining is cut square between the vertical linings and blocked to the head, as shown in Figs. 24 and 25. Sometimes a tongue is prepared on the ends about $\frac{1}{4}$ in. long, to engage with a groove in the edge of the vertical linings, to prevent the top lining from twisting. Usually, however, a skew nail in the top edge is considered satisfactory in conjunction with the blocks.

Outside Linings are usually $\frac{5}{8}$ in. wider than the

inside linings, because they project that amount over
the face of the pulley stile as a guide for the sash.
They are ploughed to receive a tongue on the pulley
stiles. The inside edge of the linings may be square,
as in Fig. 24, or it may be moulded, as in Fig. 25.
When it is moulded, it has the moulding removed where

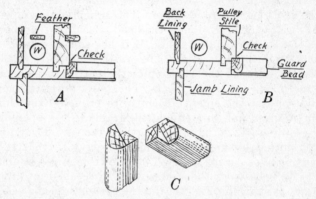

Fig. 32. Checked and Mitred Beads

it meets the sill and top lining. In the latter case the
intersection of the mouldings is mitred.

Parting Beads are thin slips, 1 in. by $\frac{1}{2}$ in., placed
between the sashes. They fit into grooves in the pulley
stiles and often in the head. They should fit tightly, so
that nailing can be avoided as far as possible. Nails
through the bead, which is usually only $\frac{3}{8}$ in. or $\frac{5}{16}$ in.
finish, weaken the bead and cause it to break easily
when it is being removed for rehanging.

Inner Beads, often called *staff, guide,* or *guard* beads,
are usually 1 in. by $\frac{3}{4}$ in. They break the joint between
the pulley stile and the lining. Sometimes the stile is
rebated, or *checked,* to receive the guard bead, as shown
in Fig. 32. This ensures the correct refixing of the bead

after hanging the sashes. For good-class work the guard beads are fixed by brass screws with cups, so that they can be removed easily. Mitred corners are often used, as shown in Fig. 32, *C*. There are many variations for the bead on the sill. If it is bevelled, as shown in Fig. 33, *A*, the sash wedges on to the bead when it is closed. This prevents the vibration of the sash. It is not necessary to remove the bottom guard bead when hanging the sashes, hence, it is sometimes

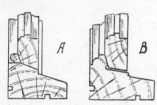

FIG. 33. BEVELLED BEADS   FIG. 34. VENTILATION BEAD

stuck on the sill, as shown in Fig. 33, *B*. The objection to this, however, is the large size of stuff required.

Ventilation Beads are bottom beads increased in width. They are used so that if the lower sash is raised a little, the ventilation will take place at the meeting rails without the discomfort of a draught at the bottom. Examples are shown in Figs. 24, 25, and 34. The latter shows a bevelled bead to prevent the vibration of the sash, without detriment to the paint. If the bead is over 2 in. wide it should be provided with small tenons at the end, and corresponding mortises should be made in the pulley stile ; this is to prevent the bead from twisting.

Parting Slips, or feathers, are used to separate the weights, so that they will not knock against each other as they ascend and descend. They are hung from the head on a stout nail, or a wooden pin, so that they swing loosely in the box. They are inserted in a slot in the head, as shown in Figs. 24 and 31. The usual dimensions are about 2 in. by $\frac{3}{8}$ in., and they are left " off the saw."

The Back Lining is a rough piece about $\frac{3}{8}$ in. thick, nailed on to the edge of the outside lining and inserted into a groove in the inside lining, as shown in Figs. 23 and 32. For inferior work they are nailed on the edges of both linings, but this method is liable to split

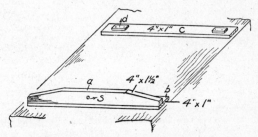

FIG. 35. ASSEMBLING SASH FRAME

the back lining as it seasons. It is better to use short lengths of wide, thin stuff and to nail them lengthwise across the box.

Assembling the Frame. The stiles are wedged and nailed in the trenches prepared in the sill. The stiles should be " out of wind," and it is often necessary to adjust the trenches, when the sill is twisted, to correct the stiles. The head is next nailed on to the stiles. Two bearers are nailed to the bench, as shown in Fig. 35. The piece a is fixed securely to piece b, and it is bored for a strong screw s. Piece c is nailed to the bench, so that it is " out of wind " with b.

Squaring the Frame. The skeleton frame is laid on the bearers with the sill resting on piece b, and the sill is screwed firmly to piece a. When the frame has been tested for squareness, as shown in Fig. 36, the two blocks *d* are nailed to the bearer *c* to keep the frame square. To square the frame, it is necessary to use a long lath (a parting bead is convenient), and to mark on the lath the length of one diagonal. The lath is next applied to the other diagonal, and the length is marked on the lath. If the two diagonals are equal the frame

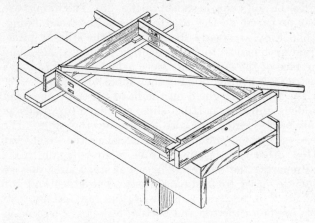

FIG. 36. SQUARING SASH FRAME

is square. If the diagonals are not equal the frame is adjusted to *half* the difference of the two marks on the lath.

Nailing the Linings. The inside linings are nailed to the stiles. Care must be taken to avoid nailing the pocket pieces. The vertical, or side, linings are fixed first, and then the head lining is cut and driven in tightly between them and nailed in position.

When the inside linings are completed, the frame is turned over and again tested for squareness. This time, however, the frame is adjusted before inserting the screw, because the head is fixed by the pieces *d*.

The outside linings project over the pulley stile,

usually ⅝ in. If the edges of the linings are square, the shoulder on the sill should have been " cut back " to suit the projection, when it was " tenoned " to receive the linings. If the edges are moulded the shoulder on the sill is level with the face of the pulley stile, and the moulding on the lining must be removed and scribed on to the sill ; this is shown in Fig. 25. The linings are also prepared at the top to receive the head lining. When they are ready for nailing to the stiles, a piece, equal in thickness to the projection, should be slid along the face of the stile. This piece acts as a gauge to give the required projection, as the linings are nailed.

The blocks are glued on the head to secure the head linings, and the parting slips are fixed in position. The back linings are also nailed on the sides. The beads are fitted round the frame when the sashes are fitted, otherwise they have to be removed again.

Preparing the Sashes. The usual stock sizes of sash stuff are used for ordinary work. The stiles and top rail are 2 in. by 2 in., and the bottom rail 3 in. by 2 in. The joints for the top and bottom rails are the same as for the sashes already described. There is considerable difference in the construction of the joints for the meeting rails. It is better to prepare *joggles,* or horns, on the ends of the stiles, so that the meeting rail can be wedged. This is shown in Fig. 37, which shows the meeting rail for the top sash. The bottom rail is increased in width when a ventilation bead is used.

The Meeting Rails should have a bevelled and rebated meeting joint, so that it is dustproof when fastened. The rebate also prevents interference with the fastener from the outside. The projection of the bevelled part over the face of the sash is equal to the thickness of the parting bead. The top meeting rail is rebated for the glass, but the bottom meeting rail has a plough groove only for the glass. The groove is shown in Figs. 24 and 25. A rebate would not be convenient because it would be covered by the top meeting rail.

The tenons on the meeting rails are practically forked tenons, due to the projection of the rail over the stile. A small portion a, about $\frac{1}{4}$ in., is removed from the face of the stile. If the projecting part of the meeting rail

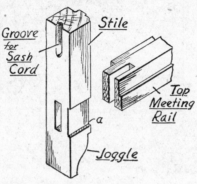

Fig. 37. Details for Meeting Rail

were cut to pass over the face of the stile, it would be too weak, and would break away. Hence, it must be let into the stile to strengthen it, as shown at a, Fig. 37.

Dovetailed tenons are used when there is no joggle. Fig. 38 shows the usual type of dovetailed joint. It is shown from the rebate side at A, when it is assembled, and from the moulded side at B, when the two pieces are apart. The illustration at B shows the scribing s running through on the rail as for a machine-made scribing. Usually, however, the scribing is prepared by hand, as in Fig. 4, B, and the moulding at the end of the stile is removed. The thickness of meeting rails is generally between $1\frac{1}{2}$ in. and $2\frac{1}{4}$ in.

The Joggles, see Fig. 37, are usually from 2 in. to 3 in.

in length, and they may be very varied in design, according to the quality of the work. They strengthen the sash considerably in addition to improving the

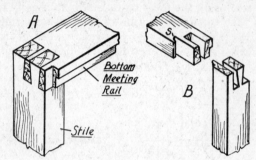

FIG. 38. JOINT FOR MEETING RAIL

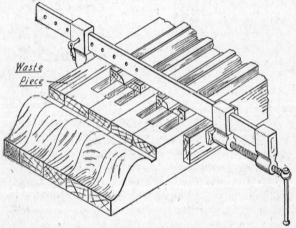

FIG. 39. PREPARING JOGGLES

appearance. It is usual to cramp together a number of stiles and to form the joggles on them in one operation, as shown in Fig. 39.

Bars are very often used for ornamentation and for

decreasing the size of the panes of glass. The preparation of the bars is the same as previously explained for sash doors and fast sheets. It is usual, however, to make a through tenon, instead of a stub tenon, because of the thinner stiles. If the tenons of the bars run through for wedging they can be straightened, if necessary, when driving in the wedges. This is very important for single bars. A judicious driving of the wedges will straighten a bar, no matter how much it is curved.

Wedging Up. The joints are glued, or painted if the sashes are exposed to the weather, and wedged up. The corners should be pinned, especially if paint is used. The most convenient method of wedging up the sashes is to place two strong cramps on the bench with the jaws upwards. A suitable cramp for the purpose is shown in Fig. 6, "Workshop Equipment." The two cramps should be screwed on the bench at the correct distance apart, so that they are in position for a number of sashes of the same size. This method enables one to use a sash cramp on the top for wedging up the bars. If the sash has no bar, a stiff piece of material should be placed across the sash, in the rebates, to prevent the cramps from bending the stiles. Wooden cramps for wedging up the sashes were shown in Fig. 9, "Workshop Equipment." The illustration also shows' the method of wedging up the sashes, which is also applicable to the iron cramps, as explained above.

Cleaning Off. When the glue is hard, the sashes are cleaned off. The ends of the tenons and the horns of the stiles are sawn off. A small part of the projection on the meeting rails is removed, equal to the width of the projection of the parting bead. The grooves for the sash cords are made about half of the length of the stile. Sometimes the groove is deeper and shorter, and continued with a hole bored down the stile to receive the cord. This is terminated by a hole bored with a centre bit. The cord is passed down the vertical hole, and a knot is made on the end of the cord to rest in the hole in the edge. This makes a secure fixing for the cord, but it is seldom applied because of the work entailed in preparing the hole down the stile. The usual method of securing the cord is to fix it by clout nails in the semicircular groove, shown in Figs. 37 and 40.

Fitting the Sashes. If the sashes have been made to the correct size, they should not require any planing on the edges except for cleaning up the ends of the tenons and horns. Usually the sashes are prepared for fitting into the frame before the frame is assembled. The sashes are then tested for height, and a little adjustment is made in the pulley stiles if it is necessary.

The frame is laid on the bench, outside downwards, and the sashes are tested for width. If any reduction is necessary, the sash is placed in the vice while planing the edges. The top sash is fitted first, and then the parting beads are fixed in position and the bottom sash is fitted. The clearance in width should be about $\frac{1}{8}$ in. to allow for three coats of paint on the pulley stiles.

When the sashes have been fitted, they are usually removed from the frame and numbered so that there is no difficulty in finding the position again. The guard beads are next fitted round the frame. Both the frame and sashes should be primed before sending them to the job.

Fixing the Frames. The sill is bedded in white lead and oil, and the frame is bedded on the brickwork with hair mortar or oil putty, as previously explained. The sill is fixed by folding wedges. If there is a wooden lintol, then the top should be fixed by two 3 in. by 1 in. pieces pressed against the outside lining, as shown at *a* in Fig. 24. Large frames should have holdfasts on each side to assist in fixing the frame, unless jamb linings fixed to wall plugs are used.

Hanging the Sashes. When the sashes have been glazed they are tested for weight, and suitable weights selected. The combined weight of the two top weights should be slightly heavier than the sash, so that they will keep the sash closed. For the same reason the bottom weights should be slightly less in weight than the sash. The friction on the sides will hold the sashes when they are open.

Use of Mouse. The beads and pockets are removed and a *mouse* is used to pass a piece of string, to which the sash cord is attached, over the pulley. The mouse is a piece of lead, or a short length of chain, fixed securely to the string. It is usual to make the mouse from a piece of sheet lead about 3 in. by $\frac{1}{2}$ in. The lead is rolled and *beaten* round the end of the string in the form of a cylinder 3 in. long and about $\frac{1}{4}$ in. diameter.

The weight of the mouse carries the string down the box until it can be pulled out at the pocket, followed by the sash cord. The weights are attached to the ends of the cords and lifted to the top of the box. A clout nail is used to nail the cord temporarily to the pulley stile until it is fixed to the sash. The outside cords are nailed to the top sash, as shown in Fig. 40, and the temporary nails removed so that the sash can slide into its position. The pockets and parting beads are replaced and then the procedure is repeated for the bottom sash.

Threading Cords. It is best to commence threading the cords over the pulleys in the following order: (1) left hand inside, (2) right hand inside, (3) left hand outside, (4) right hand outside. The weight is attached to the last cord and pulled up the box, and then the cord is nailed temporarily to the stile and cut to length. The procedure is repeated for each cord in turn, in the reverse order to that in which they were threaded through the pulleys.

When the sashes are hung the guard beads are fixed by nails or screws. Sufficient clearance must be given to allow for the easy running of the sash. This is best obtained by inserting a try square blade between the sash and the bead.

Length of Cords. If the cords for the top sash are too long, the weights will rest on the sill and prevent the

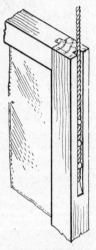

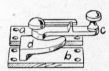

FIG. 41. SASH FASTENER

FIG. 40. NAILING SASH CORD

FIG. 42. DIAGRAM OF VENETIAN WINDOW

sash from keeping closed. If the bottom cords are too short, the weights will arrive at the pulleys before the sash is resting on the sill. For these reasons it is usual to make the top cords a little shorter and the bottom cords a little longer than the actual requirements.

A Sash Fastener, Fig. 41, is used to secure the sashes when they are closed. The plate a, which carries the latch c, is fixed to the meeting rail of the top sash. The plate b, which carries the catch d, is screwed to the inside meeting rail. There are other designs, but they usually work on the same principle.

Mullion Windows. When a frame is too wide for one pair of vertical sliding sashes, it is usual to make vertical divisions in the frame. These vertical divisions are known as *mullions*, and there may be either one or two in a frame. The usual arrangement is shown in

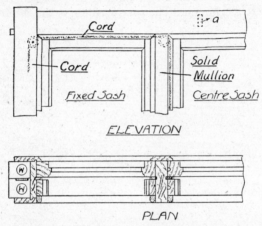

ELEVATION

PLAN

Fig. 43. Details for Solid Mullion

Fig. 42, which shows two mullions. It is generally called a venetian window. The mullions may be either solid or boxed. Solid mullions are used where the maximum amount of light is required and where economy is an important consideration.

Solid Mullions. When solid mullions are used, the centre sashes only can be hung. The side sashes have to be fixed, but only lightly, so that they can be removed for re-hanging centre sashes when necessary. The cords are attached to the centre sashes and pass over the top of the side sashes just under the pulley stile head. This requires the pulleys to be placed at the top of the mullions and stiles, as shown in Figs. 43 and 44. Special pulleys may be obtained for the purpose ; but ordinary pulleys may be used by breaking off the top part of the flange. Sufficient of the flange should be retained to engage in the trenching in the head, because the screw hole at the top has been broken away.

The details for mullion windows are the same as those already explained. The solid mullion is the same width

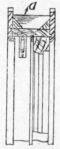 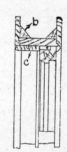

FIG. 44. SECTION
THROUGH CENTRE
SASH

FIG. 45. SECTION
THROUGH FIXED
SASH

as the sill less the thickness of the outside lining. It is tenoned through the sill and often through the head. Fig. 43 shows the head of half of the window and a sectional plan. The method of hiding the cords is shown in Fig. 45. A wide cover bead c is used which is grooved for the inside cord and moulded on the edge to mitre with the side guard beads, as shown in Fig. 46. The top fixed sash is rebated for the outside cord. The rebate should not be more than $\frac{1}{2}$ in. deep, so that the wide bead will cover the rebate.

The top linings run across the window, between the side linings. In addition to the blocks b, Fig. 45, it is necessary to strengthen the top linings by *stiffeners a,*

Figs. 43 and 44, because they have no support, except at the ends, beyond the thickness of the pulley stile head. In good work the head is increased to 2 in. in thickness, so that the pieces *a* are unnecessary.

Boxed Mullions. In better-class work it is usual to hang all the sashes. This requires a boxed mullion, so that it can carry weights in the same way as the side boxes. The construction of a boxed mullion is shown by a sectional plan, and an elevation of the box with

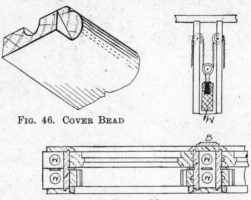

FIG. 46. COVER BEAD

FIG. 47 BOXED MULLION

the linings removed, in Fig. 47. The arrangement shown only allows for one weight serving for the sashes on each side of it.

Double Weights. When double weights are used for balancing two sashes, as shown in Fig. 47, it is necessary to have a pulley at the top of the weight instead of a hole. The cord is passed over the pulley in the stile, under the pulley in the weight, and over the opposite stile pulley. The weight is usually made of lead to obtain the necessary weight and so that the pulley can be moulded in the molten lead. It is usually square in section.

The disadvantage of this method lies in the continuous cord, which entails the rehanging of the sashes on each side of the mullion when it breaks. Also, when one sash is heavier than the other, the heavy sash has a tendency to control the movement of the lighter sash.

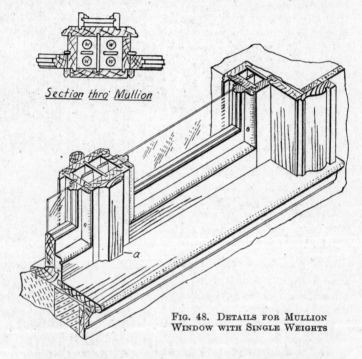

Section thro' Mullion

FIG. 48. DETAILS FOR MULLION WINDOW WITH SINGLE WEIGHTS

Boxed Mullions with Single Weights. The best method of hanging the sashes in a mullion window is by single weights. The details for this type of window, where they differ from the preceding examples, are shown in Fig. 48. The mullion is very wide because it is arranged for four weights. Usually the wide linings are relieved by cover boards, in the form of panels, as shown at *a*. The outside may have stone or cast-iron mullions to relieve the plainness and to support the head if it is of stone. Sometimes built-up pilasters are formed, as shown in the alternative section, through the mullion, or the linings may be sunk moulded at the centre for relief.

A central lining and parting slips are used to divide the box into four compartments, as shown in Fig. 48.

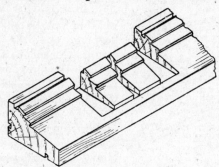

FIG. 49. PREPARING SILL

The remainder of the details are similar to those already described. The pulley stiles are usually $\frac{7}{8}$ in. thick to keep the mullion as narrow as possible.

The Sill is often prepared as shown in Fig. 49. The trenchings, or housings, do not go through on the face. A groove is formed to receive a tongue on the back of the outside lining. The pulley stiles are wedged in the usual way, and a trench is formed for the central lining. If the outside linings run over the sill, in the same way as the inside linings, they help to tie together the frame. This is an advantage, as the pulley stiles are not tenoned to the sill and head ; and it also makes a stronger job, but it breaks the continuity of the front edge of the sill.

Wide Mullions of brick or stone require separate frames. The frames are prepared in the ordinary way, as shown in Fig. 24. The joints between the frames on the inside are covered by built-up pilasters, or wide cover boards with sunk panels and moulded edges.

Weather Bars. In public buildings and good-class work generally, a weather bar is sometimes fitted to the bottom sash. Fig. 50 shows Elliott's patent weather bar. In addition to keeping out the driving rain it strengthens the sash against the pressure of the wind, and also allows for the condensation to run outside. Vertical holes are bored from a groove in the top edge of the rail, which allows the condensation to run into the steel, zinc, or brass channel from which it escapes on to the weathered sill. The details are also shown in Fig. 63.

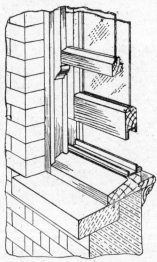

FIG. 50. ELLIOTT'S WEATHER BAR

Segmental Heads. For flat segmental arches, it is usual to follow the outline of the brick arch with the outside lining and the bottom edge of the top rail. All the other details of the frame and sashes are as previously described. Fig. 51 shows the inside and outside elevations of the top part of a window with a segmental head. The beads and linings have been removed on the inside to show the construction of the sash. If the outside lining a is very wide, it should be tongued into the side lining to prevent it from twisting.

The Top Rail *b* generally has two tenons, as shown in Fig. 52, and it is usual to form the haunch as for door framing.

Semicircular and elliptical heads present many difficulties not entailed in the previous examples. All the

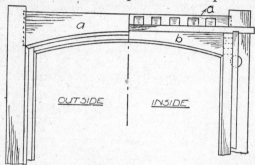

Fig. 51. Segmental-headed Sash and Frame

members above the springing are curved to follow the outline of the arch. Fig. 53 shows the elevation and vertical section of a semicircular headed sash and frame. The lower part has been omitted because the details are the same as for the ordinary sash and frame shown in Fig. 24. The inside lining and the sash have been removed to show the method of construction. Pictorial views are given in Fig. 54 to show the method of making the joints at the springing.

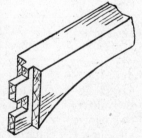

Fig. 52. Details for Top Rail

The Head is cut from the solid in the example; but very often, especially for hardwoods, it is bent round a drum in the form of a veneer. The thickness is built up in three pieces, glued and screwed together. It is necessary to break the joints, as shown in Figs. 53 and 54. The number of joints depends upon the size of the frame. They are arranged to avoid a large amount of cross-grain which is always present, more or less in circular work cut from the solid. The position of the

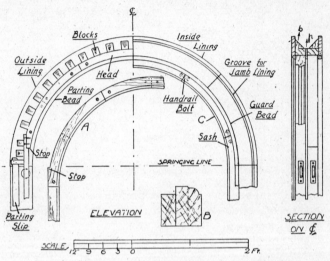

FIG. 53. SEMICIRCULAR-HEADED SASH AND FRAME

joints is also controlled by the width of the material available, from which the curved pieces are cut. If the material is very wide, there is always the danger of the curved ribs altering in shape due to shrinkage, although the building-up in three thicknesses counteracts this to a large extent.

A Templet, or pattern, is made from the full-size drawing of the elevation of the head. The templet is equal in length to the distance between two joints in the head. The required number of pieces for the head are cut to the templet ; and then the joints are broken, or crossed, by commencing at the stop with a full piece on one edge, Fig. 54, and a half-piece on the other edge.

The Parting Bead forms the middle piece of the three thicknesses, as shown at p in the vertical section. This requires a separate templet because it is of a less radius than the head on the inside. The joint is intermediate between the joint of the outside pieces of the head.

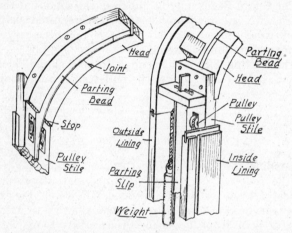

FIG. 54. DETAILS FOR CIRCULAR-HEADED FRAME

The separate pieces are glued and screwed together, so that the parting bead goes down to the springing. The remainder of the head stops a few inches above the springing to form a stop for the sash. If the stop were omitted, the sash would bang on the crown when being closed, which would probably break the glass. A corresponding shoulder is formed on the sash.

The Pulley Stiles are tongued into the linings in the usual way, but the tongues are omitted on the head because of the labour entailed in making the grooves in the linings. The stiles are carried up above the springing and are screwed to the head, as shown in Figs. 53 and 54.

The Linings are made in several pieces to suit the width of the stuff from which they have to be cut, and also to prevent distortion through shrinkage. They are grooved at the joints for cross-tongues, as shown in Fig. 54, to prevent them from twisting.

The Guard Beads may be cut from the solid, but they are usually steamed and bent to the required shape. They can be fixed securely, as it is not necessary to remove them for rehanging the sashes.

The Parting Slip is suspended from a special block which is glued and fixed to the pulley stiles and linings.

FIG. 55. METHOD OF BENDING HEAD

Bending the Head. When the head has to be bent to the required curvature, it is necessary to form a series of trenches on the back, as shown in Fig. 55. The trenches are formed by the drunken saw to within $\frac{1}{8}$ in. or $\frac{3}{16}$ in. from the face. It is necessary to make the piece sufficiently flexible to bend to the required shape. The piece is then bent round a *drum*, or centre, and secured at the ends. Blocks are glued and driven into the trenches. The blocks are equal in length to the width of the head. They are tapered a little to fit the trenches, which are wedge-shaped when the head is bent round the drum. When the glue is hard, the head is removed from the drum and fixed to the stiles in the same way as the head cut from the solid. The parting bead is glued and fixed to the head without a groove. It may be cut from the solid or it may be steamed and bent ; the latter method is usually adopted.

Veneered Head. For expensive hardwoods, it is usual to veneer the head. A thin piece of veneer is cut to width and bent round a drum. Blocks are then glued on the back of the veneer and to each other, thus building up the head to the required thickness. A piece of canvas is usually glued over the blocks to prevent the head from springing out of shape when it is released from the drum.

Further details and explanations for the construction of circular work will be given in a special section.

The Sash top rail is *built up* as described for the head. A little more than half of the top rail of the sash is shown at *A*, Fig. 53. It is built up in two thicknesses, as shown at *B*. The joint, in the thickness, is made on the rebate, as shown by the full line. The dotted line shows an alternative method, which is not so good, because it requires a double sticking for rebate and ovolo. If the joint is made on the rebate, then the rebate is formed by a less width of material.

The *half-piece* used to break the joints is part of the stile. This helps to keep the shape of the top rail. A sash of this description usually has bars to strengthen the sash and to help it to retain its shape ; although once it is glazed and the putty has hardened, there is little danger of the sash altering in shape.

When the top rail is cut from the solid, as shown by the half-sash at *C* in Fig. 53, the joints are made with small handrail bolts. Sometimes dowels only are used, but they are not satisfactory. Hardwood keys may be used for big stuff, but they are not convenient for ordinary sash stuff. The stile should be continued above the springing to the first joint.

CASEMENT WINDOWS

Windows with solid frames and hinged sashes are called *casement windows*. They may have any number of sashes up to eight, but four or six is the usual number. Fig. 56 shows a casement window with four sashes or casements for a recessed opening with wood lintel. If it is built-in with the brickwork, the stiles should be tenoned into head and sill as in Figs. 57 and 67. The number of sashes that are hinged depends upon the amount of ventilation required.

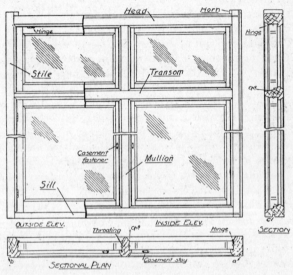

FIG. 56. CASEMENT WINDOWS, SASHES OPENING OUTWARDS

Arrangement of Casements. The casements may be arranged to open inwards or outwards; the latter are more satisfactory for keeping out the driving rain. A sudden storm, however, is liable to break an open sash off its hinges unless it is securely stayed; also, sashes opening outwards are difficult to clean when they are on upper storeys.

Casements opening inwards interfere with the curtains

and other window furnishings, but they are generally preferred if the sill is made watertight.

CASEMENTS OPENING OUTWARDS

Fig. 56 shows the details for a casement window with the sashes opening outwards. The views show the outside and inside elevations, with the vertical and horizontal sections. The details apply to any number of casements.

The Frame consists of 5 in. by 3 in. stiles, head, and sill. The width of the stuff usually depends upon the jambs and the size of the frame. In addition there is a 5 in. by 3 in. transom, and a 5 in. by 3 in. or $2\frac{1}{2}$ in. mullion. A frame with six sashes would have two similar mullions.

The head, sill, and transom may be tenoned into the stiles, as shown in the illustration, but it is better for the sill to run through, as in Fig. 57. If the head has to carry any load it should run through also, so that the load is carried by the vertical members, instead of by the tenons of the top rail. Double tenons should be used; but for cheap work one tenon, about $1\frac{1}{4}$ in. thick, is considered satisfactory when assisted by nails.

The Sill should be of teak or oak. It should be weathered, double sunk, and throated; and it should be ploughed for water bar and window bottom. Fig. 57 shows an isometric view of the hanging corner of the sash with the details for the sill. The latter are also shown in the section *A*. The moulding on the edge depends upon the quality of the work. It may be a chamfer, ogee, ovolo, or lamb's tongue.

The Stiles are rebated, throated, and moulded on both edges. Fig. 58 is a horizontal section through the stile showing the throatings and the method of hanging the bottom sash. It is not usual to employ two throatings; either *a* or *b* is considered satisfactory for ordinary purposes. The use of the throating is to prevent capillary attraction. The stiles should be ploughed for the jamb linings, as shown at *a* in Fig. 56. The dovetail groove shown at *b* is satisfactory for plaster.

The Head is prepared in the same way as the stiles. The mouldings should be mitred, especially if only one tenon is used. If double tenons are used the mouldings may be scribed, but they are usually mitred.

The Transom requires considerable preparation. It should be double sunk on the top to receive the bottom

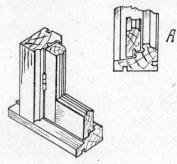
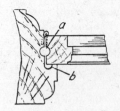

FIG. 57. SASH OPENING OUTWARDS

FIG. 58. DETAIL FOR STILE, SASH OPENING OUTWARDS

rail of the sash. An alternative section is shown in Fig. 59. The moulding on the front edge is omitted and a throating used instead. This would give greater protection to the top edge of the sash, from the driving rain.

The Mullions are tenoned into the transom. They are moulded and rebated in the same way as the stiles.

CASEMENTS OPENING INWARDS

Fig. 60 shows the vertical section for a casement window with the sashes opening inwards. The general arrangement of the frame is the same as in Fig. 56, except that the rebates for the sashes are on the inside of the frame. The difficulty of this frame is in the details for the sill. It is a difficult matter to make the sill watertight except by the aid of metal water bars. The dimensions of the various members of the frame are the same as for Fig. 56.

The Sill requires careful preparation to keep out the driving rain. The best method is to form the sill so that it collects the water and then allows it to escape by

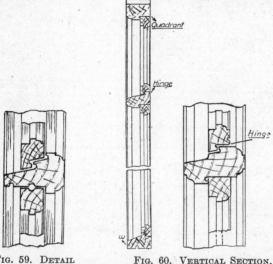

FIG. 59. DETAIL
FOR TRANSOM

FIG. 60. VERTICAL SECTION,
CASEMENTS OPENING INWARDS

means of weep holes. Three different details for the sill are given in Figs. 60 and 61, and other methods will be shown for French casements. Fig. 60 shows the arrangement for thin frames where the sash is flush with the frame. Fig. 61 shows an isometric view, with the sill cut through a weep hole, and a section at *B* for the same detail. An alternative is shown at *A*, where the moulding on the sill is the same as that on the stiles. In every case the water is collected in a condensation groove and allowed to escape through the weep holes. The section at *B* is better for collecting the condensation as well as the driving rain.

The Weep Holes should be about $\frac{5}{16}$ in. diameter. They should have a piece of brass tubing driven tightly

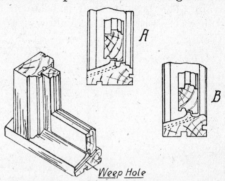

Weep Hole

FIG. 61. SASH OPENING INWARDS

into the hole so that it projects about $\frac{1}{4}$ in. over the face of the sill. The other end is filed to the outline of the groove. For cheap work the weep hole is charred with a piece of red-hot wire.

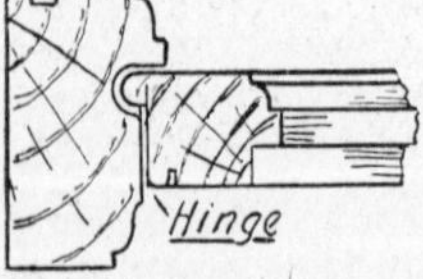

Hinge

FIG. 62. DETAIL FOR STILE, SASH OPENING INWARDS

The Stiles are prepared as shown in Fig. 61. The details are the same as in Fig. 58, except that the rebate is reversed. An alternative section is given in Fig. 62, but the section is draught-proof rather than proof against capillary attraction.

The Transom is usually prepared as in Fig. 60. An enlarged detail is also given, showing the frame projecting over the face of the sashes. If required the top inside edge could be prepared with a condensation groove with weep holes to carry away the water, but it is not usual.

Sash Details. The construction of the sashes is the same as for those already described. It is usual in good work to throat the stiles and top rail, as shown in Fig. 58, especially when the sashes open outwards. The

FIG. 63. CASEMENT OPENING OUTWARDS

FIG. 64. CASEMENT OPENING INWARDS

throating is usually omitted when the sashes open inwards, although it should be formed on the frame, as shown in Fig. 61. A small weep hole should be provided for sashes opening outwards, in case the driving rain finds its way to the throating on the top rail.

The bottom rails, both for top and bottom sashes, should be rebated to engage with the double sinking on the sill and transom. A small throating should be provided on the outside edge of the bottom sashes opening inwards, as shown in Figs. 60 and 61 *A*.

For narrow windows the mullion is often omitted below the transom. The stiles of the lower sashes meet together with a hook joint. This is satisfactory for good work in hardwood ; but not for cheap work, as the weather influences the joint and prevents it from closing satisfactorily.

Hanging the Sashes. The bottom sashes are hung on the stiles, usually by a pair of 3 in. butt hinges. The edge of the stile is beaded and the knuckle of the hinge

FIG. 65
CASEMENT
FASTENER

is let entirely into the bead, whilst the flange only is let into the frame. This is shown in Fig. 58. When the top sashes open outwards they must be hung at the top. If they open inwards, they should be hung at the bottom. Sometimes pivots are used, as previously explained.

Figs. 63 and 64 are pictorial views showing outward and inward opening sashes respectively. They show the application of Elliott's weather bar to casement windows. Fig. 63 shows the arrangement for carrying away the condensation. A vertical hole is bored through the rail, which allows the water to run into the metal trough on the sill. A hole in the trough allows the water to escape on to the weathered sill.

Fastening the Sashes. The bottom sashes are secured by casement fasteners, Fig. 65. The catch on the plate *b*, which is fixed to the frame, is inverted so that the weight of the handle *h* keeps the latch engaged with the catch. The plate *a*, which carries the cranked handle, is fixed to the casement. If the frame projects over the face of the sashes, as in Figs. 56 and 61, a slot is mortised in the frame to receive the latch. In place of the catch a slotted plate is screwed over the mortise.

Casement Stays, Fig. 66, are used to keep the sash in position when it is open. The plate *b* is fixed to the frame and the plate *a* to the sash. The stay is held in the required position by the screw *c*.

METAL CASEMENTS

The tendency to-day is to use metal casements in preference to wooden ones. Owing to the small size of the steel members they have not a satisfactory appearance unless they are supplemented by a wood surround. The illustrations on pages 212, 213, apply to this type

FIG. 66. CASEMENT STAY

of window made by the Crittall Manufacturing Co., of Braintree. The wooden surrounds are also made by Crittalls. If more imposing woodwork is desired than the standardized sections supplied with the casements, other details may be used, provided the correct sizes for the metal casements are retained.

Metal Casements with Wood Surround. Fig. 67 shows a common type of metal casement. The large sash may be fitted with projecting hinges if required, so that the arm may be placed between the wood stile and the hanging stile of the casement ; this makes the window easy to clean from the inside. The surround stiles and head are of $3\frac{1}{2}$ in. by $2\frac{1}{2}$ in. stuff, and the sill is of 5 in. by $2\frac{1}{2}$ in.

The details of the standard window are shown in Fig. 68. The channels of the casement should be filled with mastic cement before being placed in position in the surround. The casement is screwed in position, care being taken not to force the metal-work out of shape. The given sections are taken through the fixed panes.

Alternative details are given in Fig. 69. In this case the sections are taken through the hanging casements. These details show the preparation of the woodwork for the casements, from other details than the standard pattern of surround. More elaborate details may be used, and any sizes of timbers. The illustrations show the method of measuring for the metal casements,

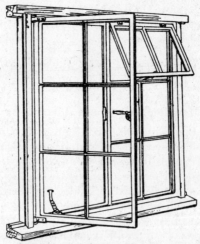

FIG. 67. METAL CASEMENT WITH WOOD SURROUND

which may be obtained in a large number of sizes and with various arrangements of the opening sections.

FRENCH CASEMENTS

When the lower casements are arranged to serve as doors, they are called *French casements*. They may be arranged to open inwards or outwards. The details vary very little from those already given. An example of good-class French casements to open inwards is shown in Fig. 70.

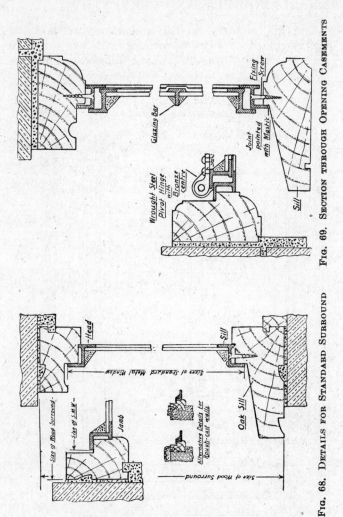

Glazing Bar

Fixing Screw

Joint pointed with Mastic

Sill

Wrought Steel Pivot Hinge with Bronze centre

Fig. 69. Section through Opening Casements

Head

Sill

Sizes of Standard Metal Window

Size of Wood Surround

Size of S.M.W.

Jamb

Oak Sill

Alternative Details for Rough-cast walls

Size of Wood Surround

Fig. 68. Details for Standard Surround

The Sill requires careful preparation to make it watertight. Two different arrangements are shown in Fig. 71. A projecting metal bar is shown at *B* to form the rebate, and a throated weather board is used to

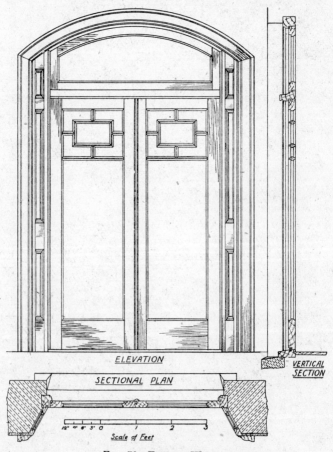

ELEVATION

SECTIONAL PLAN

VERTICAL SECTION

Scale of Feet

Fig. 70. French Window

throw the water away from the rebate. Sometimes a channel is formed behind the metal bar to hold any water that may get past the metal bar. A weep hole is made to carry away the water. Fig. 71, *A*, shows Adams' patent water bar, which is an efficient rain and draught excluder. A metal bar *a* is screwed to the door, and *c* is screwed to the sill. A

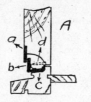

FIG. 71. DETAILS FOR SILL

flap *b* is hinged to *c* and falls flat on to *c* when the door is open. When the door closes, a projecting spur *d* engages with *b* so that it is lifted up and pressed against *a*.

The Fanlight should be arranged to open. It could

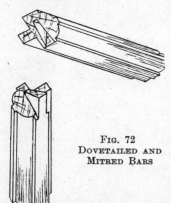

FIG. 72
DOVETAILED AND
MITRED BARS

be strengthened by bars if required, or ornamented by bars as arranged in the doors. Instead of a quadrant, it is usual to operate the fanlight by cranked levers for this class of work. The levers are fixed, one to each stile, on the casement, and connected up with rods to one side, so that the mechanism is operated by a box key at a reasonable height from the floor.

The Bars in the doors require no explanation except for the mitred corners. Fig. 72 shows one method of forming the angles. The dovetail is hidden, so that the joint has the appearance of being mitred only.

A hardwood slip or feather should be used in addition, for the rebates.

A Hook Joint is used for the meeting stiles of the doors, and a planted rebate is used as an additional precaution against the weather. It is not necessary, however, with a well-fitted hook joint.

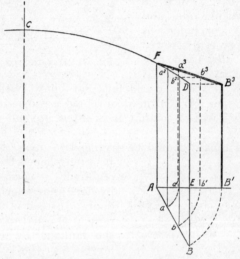

FIG. 73 SHAPE OF JAMB LINING

The Hanging Stiles can be arranged as shown in Fig. 62. Three hinges should be used to each stile.

The Finishings. The splayed jambs are fitted with panelled framing. The soffit, however, is level, but it is panelled to follow the arrangement on the jambs. The details are similar to those described in the section on "Doors."

The Jamb Linings should be tongued and the soffit trenched at their intersection. The method of finding the shape of the cut for the top of the jamb lining is shown in Fig. 73. The elevation of the face of half of the soffit is shown by the line CD, and the plan of the face of the jamb lining by the line AB. Part of the elevation of the jamb lining is shown at $AEDF$.

Take a number of points on AB, such as a, b. Project the points on to the intersection FD, as shown at a^2b^2. With compass on A, swing round the points a, b, B, on to AB^1, giving $Aa^1b^1B^1$. Project perpendiculars from these points to meet horizontals from a^2, b^2, D. Then F, a^3, b^3, B^3 is the outline, or true shape, of the top of the jamb lining.

Fastenings. French windows are usually secured by an *espagnolette bolt*. A good type is shown in Fig. 74. When the lever handle is turned, the bolts shoot both up and down into the sockets b which are fixed to the transom and sill respectively. If the door is very high and the stiles slender, the bolt should be provided with additional catches at a.

Combined Door and Window. Fig. 75 shows a combination of doors and window as used in modern house construction. The doors require the same details at the sill as for Fig. 70, if they open inwards. The details for the side casements are the same as in the previous examples. The sills a and d should be of oak and run through.

Fig. 74.
Espagnolette
Bolt

A nosing is tongued into a, and a plough groove in the edge of c and b gives a key for the plaster. The joint between the plaster and the stile is covered by an architrave.

Metal French Windows. Fig. 76 is an illustration of French casements in metal, made by Crittalls. The

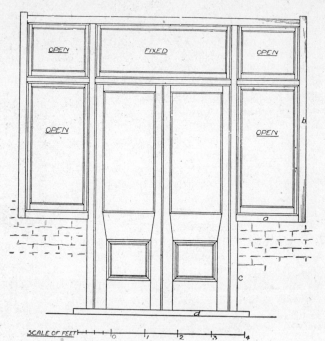

OPEN FIXED OPEN

OPEN OPEN

SCALE OF FEET 0 1 2 3 4

FIG. 75. COMBINED DOOR AND WINDOW

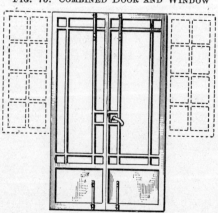

FIG. 76. METAL FRENCH WINDOW

side casements are optional, but they should be provided for ventilation. Ordinary sliding bolts are used because of the narrow meeting stiles, but a latch and lock are provided for additional security.

BAY WINDOWS

In modern buildings, bay windows are usually of the casement type, and they may be either square or octagonal in plan. If the opening is small they are sometimes arranged as the three sides of a hexagon. The details are very similar in all cases, and differ very little from the previous examples of casement windows, except at the corner posts or mullions. Fig. 77 shows an octagonal bay with casements opening outwards.

Construction. The sill is mitred at the corners, and the joints are made secure by handrail bolts. Dowels or cross-tongues should be used to prevent the joint from breaking. The jamb posts are tenoned into the head and sill, and wedged. The head may be prepared as the sill, or the joints may be halved. The transom is tenoned into the corner mullions, and the intermediate mullions are tenoned into the transom. The corner mullions are stub tenoned into the sill and head and secured by screws or coach screws.

The Corner Mullions may be formed from the solid stuff, as shown in Fig. 77. It is more usual, however, to build up the mullion, as shown in Fig. 78. A solid mullion requires the stuff to be about 6 in. by 6 in. in section, and unless it is well seasoned it is difficult to prevent it from casting and splitting as it seasons.

If formed as in Fig. 78, the two pieces are tongued and screwed together. For inferior work it is usual to plant the rebates so as to be able to use thinner stuff.

The detail at *A* shows the casements opening outwards, and that at *B* shows them opening inwards.

The detail at *C* shows the section of the sill for the sashes opening inwards.

Sometimes cover moulds are used to hide the joint

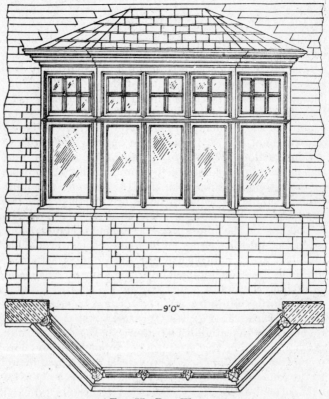

Fig. 77. Bay Window

in the mullion; they may be used both inside and outside. It is more usual, however, to make a sunk moulding on the corner, as shown in Fig. 78.

Alternative Construction. When the corner mullions

are mitred, as in Fig. 78, the sill, transom, and head
are often tenoned and wedged into them. This applies

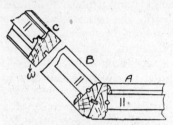

FIG. 78. DETAILS OF BAY
WINDOW

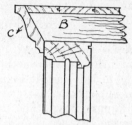

FIG. 79. HEAD OF BAY
WINDOW

more to cheap cottage work. The three sections of the
bay are wedged up as separate frames, and then the
corner posts are screwed
securely together; this
method lessens the labour
considerably.

The Head. The construction of the head of the bay
varies according to the class
of work and the conditions.
Fig. 79 shows the simplest
way of finishing the head.
The bearers *B* are supported
at the wall end by a lintel.
A cornice moulding is
mitred round the window
for ornamentation. The top
is flat and is covered
with lead, and a small
gutter is formed near the

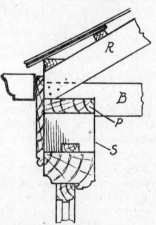

FIG. 80. HEAD OF BAY
WINDOW

wall to carry away the water. The bearers are
boarded or plastered underneath for the soffit.

An Alternative Method is shown in Fig. 80. This

method is adopted where it is required to raise the
soffit above the window head. Studs S are fixed to
the head to the required height, and a plate P is fixed
on the top of the studs to carry the bearers B and the
rafters R. Deep fascias are required to cover the studs,
or the surfaces may be plastered. Fig. 85 shows an
extension of this method of studding above the bay ;
but in this case it is intended to continue the bay to
an upper floor.

Square Bays. The details for the corner post of a
square bay are shown in Fig. 81. The description for

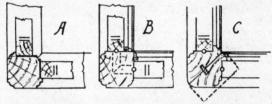

FIG. 81. DETAILS FOR SQUARE BAY

the octagonal bays applies equally to the square bays.
Fig. 81, A, shows one method of preparing the post so
that the minimum size of stuff may be used. The
reduction of the section means that the horizontal
members have to be mitred on the inside.

Two details are given at B and C for sashes opening
outwards. The rebates are shown planted at B to
reduce the section of the solid post. If the transom
has mitred stub tenons, as shown, it can be fixed by
pins, which are afterwards covered by the planted
rebates. The section at C is generally adopted, and
the pieces are often cut, as shown by the dotted rectangle, so that 3 in. deals are suitable.

Boxed Frames. Bay windows with sliding sashes
are seldom used in modern house construction. When
they are used they are generally accompanied by

heavy stone mullions and reveals. In this case the window can be constructed as three separate frames with the same details as Fig. 24.

Window Shutters. This form of window finishing is seldom used to-day. When shutters are required they are usually fixed on the wall outside, so that they lie flat to the wall when not in use. Even wall shutters,

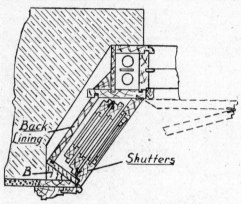

FIG. 82. WINDOW SHUTTERS

which are in the form of light batten doors, are provided more for ornamentation than for utility.

Boxed Shutters. The usual arrangement for inside shutters is shown in Fig. 82. A box is framed to receive the shutters when they are not in use. The shutters are arranged so that they will fit inside the box, and also make the required width when open. They are usually panelled and moulded for appearance, but sometimes only the one forming the jamb lining is moulded. The others, which are called *back-flaps*, are often fitted with bead-butt panels.

The horizontal section in Fig. 82 shows the method of hinging the back flaps to the front shutter, and the dotted lines show the position when the shutters are being closed. The block *B* is plugged to the brickwork and helps to carry both the box and the ground for the architrave.

There are many other arrangements for shutters. When the jambs are square to the frame instead of being splayed, the boxing is very similar in construction to Fig. 82. Sometimes the shutters are arranged to

(Crittall & Co.)

FIG. 83. BAY WINDOWS WITH METAL CASEMENTS

slide vertically and are balanced in the same way as sliding sashes.

Bay Windows with Metal Casements. Fig. 83 shows a bay window with metal casements, made by Messrs. Crittalls, Ltd. Both the casements and surrounds are standardized, but they may be obtained in many sizes. Fig. 84 shows the details for the horizontal section. The front casement is made to open but the sides are fixed. Other types of frames may be obtained with more lights and with different arrangements for the casements to open.

Square Bay. A square bay with metal casements is shown in Fig. 85A. The illustration is given because it shows several features now often adopted in modern house construction. The wings, or side casements, to

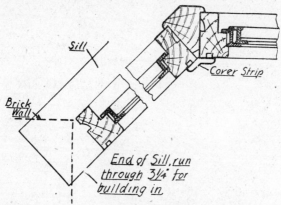

Sill

Cover Strip

Brick Wall

End of Sill, run through 3¼" for building in.

Fig. 84. Details for Bay Window with
Metal Casements

the door, and the door hood, or canopy, are very common.

Circular Bays. The details for bow windows are the same as for the foregoing example, except for the outline of the horizontal members of the frame. They are circular in plan and built up in several solid pieces. The joints are best made by handrail bolts, but they are often halved, and the segments of the sill and head are often jointed together by hardwood keys. The sections of the various members are the same as for the other types of bay windows. Sometimes the sashes are straight in plan, forming chords to the circular arcs. This eliminates much labour, but the method is only suitable for segmental, and not for semi-circular, bays.

MISCELLANEOUS WINDOWS

Stormproof Windows. Numerous firms are specializing in the mass production of casement windows,

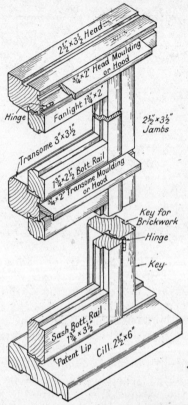

FIG. 85. STORMPROOF WINDOWS

usually described as stormproof joinery. The introduction of these windows has brought wood casements again into prominence and large numbers are used for the many housing schemes throughout the country. In many cases there is little to justify the claim beyond a free use of throatings. Several firms, however, produce windows with a rebated sash which does increase the resistance against wind and rain.

Fig. 85 shows a window of this description made by Austin of East Ham, Ltd. The projection, or lip, on the sash is patented and made possible by the use of a cranked hinge something like a box hinge. The hinges are strongly made and cadmium plated to prevent corrosion, and more screws are used than in the ordinary hinge. Another feature is the number of throatings and the free fitting of the sashes in the frame, to avoid easing in the event of expansion.

The sashes are not mortised and tenoned in the usual way, but provided with a laminated corner joint, and pinned with rust-proof pins. This increases the strength considerably, and with machines and mass production does not add to the cost, The frame may have single or double tenons and it is pinned with hardwood pins to prevent any pulling away of the joints. They are well designed and all the members are of sufficient size to withstand the rough usage associated with built-in frames. The sill is double sunk, and grooves are provided in the various members to key with the brickwork and keyed for external rendering. Hood mouldings are used to protect the tops of the sashes against rain.

Double Windows. Banks, offices, and public buildings are often fitted with double windows, sometimes called *storm sashes*. Fig. 86 shows the vertical section and horizontal section through one box, for a double window with balanced, or sliding, sashes. This type of window can only be used in walls at least 14 in. thick.

The window consists of two pairs of sliding sashes. The details are the same as Fig. 24. A parting bead

divides the two pairs of sashes. The centre parting
slip in the box is made thicker and rests in plough
grooves in the pulley stile and back lining.

Another form of double window is one that has one
pair of sliding sashes on the outside, and ordinary
casements opening inwards on the inside. This method

(*Crittall & Co.*)

Fig. 85a. Square Bay

requires a less width of box. Sometimes double casements are used, the outer ones opening outwards and
the inner ones opening inwards, but this form of window
is not generally adopted.

Double windows not only keep out the noise, dust,
and draught, but they keep the room warmer in winter
and cooler in summer.

Combined Sliding Sashes and Casement. For high
rooms in schools, hospitals, etc., windows are often
used which combine sliding sashes and casement. The
casement is at the top and opens with a quadrant.
The details are the same as for the ordinary sash and
frame, but a solid transom is introduced to serve as the

head for the sliding sashes. The casement is hinged to the transom, as shown in Fig. 87. The illustration only shows the vertical section at the transom, as all the other details have been explained.

Hoppers. The advantage of the above window is

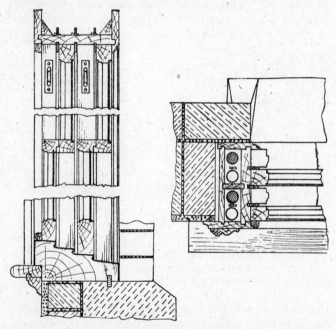

FIG. 86. DOUBLE WINDOWS

that ventilation can be obtained without draught, in inclement weather. It is usual to have hoppers at the side of the casement, as shown for fanlights in the section on "Doors." If the hopper is of wood it excludes the light, so very often it is made as a glazed sash, as shown in Fig. 88. The section of the stuff is lighter than that generally used for sashes. It is generally about 1½ in. by 1½ in. A projecting bead is fixed at the outer edge on which the casement rests.

Hospital Windows. A special form of window, called a hospital light, or hopper frame, is shown in Fig. 89. This window can be used for a less height than the combined sliding sash and casement. It consists of a series of narrow casements as long as

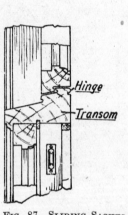

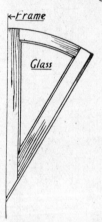

FIG. 87. SLIDING SASHES
AND CASEMENT

FIG. 88. SASH
HOPPER

the width of the window. These casements are placed one above the other for the full height of the window. Only two are shown in the illustration, but hopper frames usually have four casements about 1 ft. 6 in. high, for a window about 6 ft. 6 in. high.

The bottom sash is hung to the sill with butt hinges, but the other sashes are pivoted to the frame, so that each sash is independent of the others. The pivots are screwed at the ends of the bottom rail of each sash. When the sashes are opened they rest on beads screwed to the jamb linings, the beads thus forming hoppers. If all the sashes are opened, there is the maximum ventilation without downward draughts.

A thin metal bar is screwed on the outside of the bottom rails to keep out the driving rain when one of the sashes is open. The bar is as long as the width of the window, and it is usually of zinc.

"Austral" Windows. The "Austral" window, made

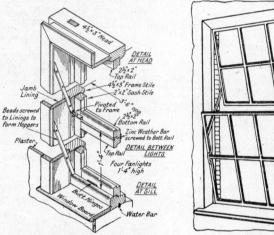

FIG. 89. HOSPITAL OR HOPPER
WINDOW

FIG. 90. "AUSTRAL"
WINDOW

by H. Hope and Sons, Birmingham, is now being used extensively in schools and hospitals. The sashes are balanced on arms so that weights, pulleys, and cords are eliminated. Fig. 90 shows a general view of the window when it is open at the centre only, while Fig. 91 shows the sashes open for maximum ventilation.

The balance arm, which is shown in the vertical section in Fig. 91, is pivoted to the frame and fixed to both sashes. The arm revolves through a quarter

circle, as shown by the dotted lines. When the sash
fastener is released on the meeting rails, the bottom
sash is lifted upwards and the two sashes swing apart
without any effort owing
to the perfect balance of
the sashes.

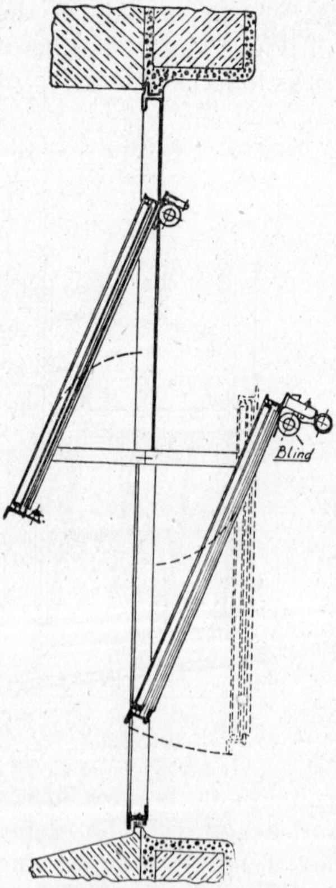

The top and bottom rails
of the sashes are provided
with rollers, so that they
move freely in the channels
of the steel frame. The
sashes are so constructed
that they stay in any re-
quired position. The illustrations show the window
without a wood surround.
Blind fixtures are provided,
as shown in Fig. 91, if
required.

Oriel Windows are ordinary bay windows supported
on brackets or corbels. They
may be semi-octagonal or
semi-square bays. Very
often the brackets supporting the bay are of a very
ornamental character.
Sometimes they are lathed,
cement rendered, and
pebble-dashed. When the
brackets are at right angles
to the wall they present no
difficulty. Brackets that are

FIG. 91. DETAILS FOR
"AUSTRAL" WINDOW

arranged for plastering, as in Fig. 92, require a
knowledge of geometry to find the true shape. The
example is rather elaborate, but it illustrates the

method of finding the true shape of the brackets better than does the usual type of window with three sides.

The illustration shows the plan and elevation of the brackets for one side of the window only. The front of the bay may be any width to suit the requirements.

Elevation of Brackets. The brackets are shown in

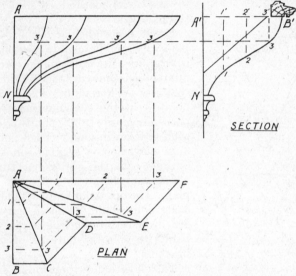

FIG. 92. BRACKETS FOR ORIEL WINDOW

plan at *AB*, *AC*, *AD*, *AE*, and *AF*. The true shape of the bracket *AB* is shown in the section at *A'B'N'*. The following describes the method of finding the elevations—

Select several points on the outline of the bracket in the section, as 1, 2, 3. Project these points on to a level line, as *A'*, *1'*, *2'*, *3'*, *B'*. Also transfer the projected points to *AB* in plan, so that *A*, 1, 2, 3, *B* is the same as *A'*, *1'*, *2'*, *3'*, *B'*. Through the points in plan, draw lines parallel to the outline of the bay so that they intersect on the plans of the brackets. Each bracket in plan will now be divided proportionately to the central bracket, as shown on the wall rib A, 1, 2, 3, F. The point 3 has been selected to show the method of drawing the parallels.

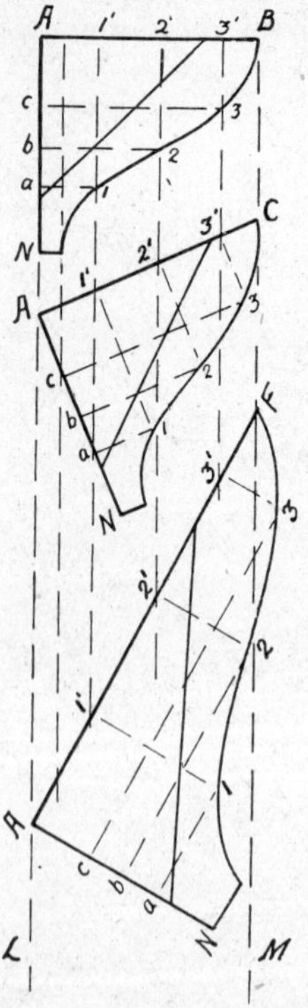

Erect perpendiculars from the points on each bracket to meet horizontal lines drawn from the same numbered point in the section; that is, a horizontal line from point 3 in the section meets the perpendiculars from point 3 on each bracket in plan. Then point 3 in elevation is a point on the outline of the bracket, from which the point was projected in plan. The operation is repeated for each point, and freehand curves are drawn through the series of points to give the outlines of the brackets.

The elevation of the window can be drawn by applying the same method.

True Shape of Brackets. Draw the true shape of the centre bracket as shown at ANB in Fig. 93; that is, copy the bracket as in the section, Fig. 92. Draw two parallel lines as AL and BM as right angles to AB. Project the points on the curve of the bracket to AN to give A, c, b, a, N. Take the length AC from plan in Fig. 92 and set it across the parallel lines AL and BM, as shown in Fig. 93.

FIG. 93. TRUE SHAPE OF BRACKETS

Draw *A N* at right angles to *A C*. Transfer the points from the bracket *A B* to the bracket *A C*, by marking the position of *A, c, b, a, N* on a piece of paper. Now project the points 1', 2', 3' from *A B* to *A C*. Draw lines at right angles to *A C* from the points 1', 2', 3'; and also at right angles to *A N* from *c, b, a*. The intersection of these lines will meet

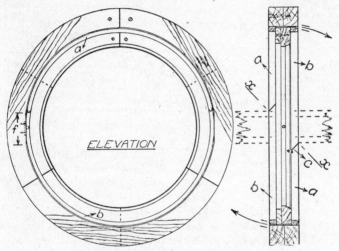

FIG. 94. BULL'S-EYE WINDOW

at points on the curve of the bracket *A N C*. Draw a free-hand curve through the points to give the required outline.

Repeat the process for each bracket in turn. *A D* and *A E* have been omitted, but the true shape of the bracket *A F* is also shown on the parallel lines *A L* and *B M*.

Pivoted Sashes. The simpler forms of pivoted sashes have already been described. Fig. 94 shows a bull's-eye window that provides a more difficult example. In this case, it is usual to fix the pivot to the frame and the socket to the sash. The illustration shows the outside elevation and a vertical section. The beads, or rebates, marked *a*, are fixed to the frame, and those marked *b* are fixed to the sash. Of course the sash opens inwards at the top. The pivots should be placed a little above the centre of the sash so that it will be self-closing, if the sash is rectangular.

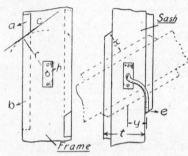

FIG. 95. PREPARING REBATES FOR PIVOTS

Method of Cutting Beads. The position of the sash is drawn when it is open at the maximum position. It may be horizontal, as shown by dotted lines in Fig. 94 ; but it is usual to have the maximum position, as shown by dotted lines in Fig. 95, so that the rain can run off freely. The side elevation of the frame and sash are shown separately in Fig. 95 for clearness. The dotted lines on the frame show the position of the sash rebates when the sash is in position and closed.

The simplest method of cutting the rebates is shown in Fig. 94. A diagonal *x–x* is drawn across the intersections of the open sash and the closed sash. The cuts for the beads are at right angles to the line *x–x*, as shown at *C*. This method requires a slot in the edge of the sash so that the sash can be slid in position over the projecting pivots.

Slotted Bead. A better method is shown in Fig. 95. In this case the beads are cut farther away from the open sash. The increased distance *x* allows for the socket in the sash to be dropped on to the pivot. The distance x should be at least equal to y. A groove e is then cut on the edge of the sash and along the bead so that the pivot can easily pass along the groove.

The cuts c for the beads should be tangential to an arc struck with a radius r from the centre of the pivot. The radius r is equal to t, which is from the centre of the groove e to the face of the outside bead.

Bull's-eye Window. The foregoing remarks apply to any form of sash pivoted horizontally. But there is another consideration with a circular sash. It is necessary to have a flat surface round the pivots on the edge of the sash and on the frame. This is shown at f in Fig. 94. The flat surface on the frame may be prepared on the solid, or it may be formed by inlaying a thin piece of hardwood. The latter is better for a softwood frame. Another method is to prepare the sash and frame circular, and then to cut off the required amount from the edge of the sash and beads, and glue the pieces to the frame.

The Beads are cut from the solid but they may be steamed and bent to the required curvature.

The Frame and the sash may be constructed as described for the semicircular sash, Fig. 54. Fig. 94 shows both frame and sash built up in two thicknesses with the joints crossed. The pieces are glued and screwed, which makes a very satisfactory job. If the frame is cut from the solid, the joints should be secured by handrail bolts or hardwood keys.

LOUVRE VENTILATOR

Ventilators take the place of windows for inaccessible positions or where the ventilation is required to be continuous. The frames are fitted with inclined boards, called *louvres*, which are arranged to keep out the driving rain. The frames may be rectangular, triangular, or circular. The first-named presents no difficulties, but the circular frame is rather difficult to construct. The geometry entailed in the circular frame is applicable to the triangular frame.

Circular Louvre Ventilator. The elevation and vertical section of a circular louvre ventilator is shown in Fig. 96. The construction of the frame is the same as

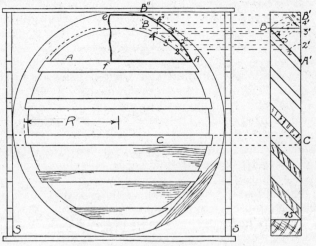

FIG. 96. CIRCULAR LOUVRE VENTILATOR

for the bull's-eye window. Handrail bolts or hardwood keys are used to make the joints if the frame is cut from the solid ; but it is easier to build up in two thicknesses and to glue and screw the pieces together, as previously described.

The Louvres. The preparation of the louvres presents some difficulty and requires a knowledge of geometry. It is necessary to find the true shape of the surface of each louvre by revolving, or rabatting, the surface into the vertical plane. The method is shown in Fig. 96, with the surface of the top louvre.

Geometrical Method. Revolve the surface of the louvre about the corner $A-A$ as though the corner were an axis, or hinge. The end view of the axis is shown at A', and the end view of the surface of the louvre is shown at $A'B$. The elevation of the end of the louvre is shown at A, 2, 3, 4, B; while the corresponding points are shown in the end view at A', 2, 3, 4, B. Revolve these points in the end view so that they are in the vertical plane at A', 2', 3', 4', B'. The points in the elevation will move at right angles to the axis $A-A$. Also the points in elevation must be on the same level as the corresponding points in the end elevation. Hence, the method of finding the position of the required points is to erect perpendiculars from the points in the elevation to meet horizontal lines drawn from the points in the end elevation. A vertical line from

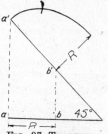

FIG. 97. TEMPLET FOR LOUVRES

4 and a horizontal line from 4' meet at a point 4''; therefore 4'' is a point on the *true shape* of the louvre. By repeating the method for each point we have a series of points A, 2'', 3'', 4'', B''. A freehand curve through these points gives the required outline.

A piece of cardboard cut to the outline will serve for both ends of the louvre. It is necessary to repeat the process for each louvre.

Practical Method. Set out the louvres on two boards, S, which are shown in Fig. 96. The boards are as wide as the thickness of the frame. Assemble the frame temporarily and place the boards on each side of the frame. The boards must be kept square and in position by nailing strips on their ends, as shown in the illustration. With a straightedge, transfer the marks for the louvres, which are on the edges of the boards, to both sides of the frame. Cut a strip of cardboard to the same shape as the section of the louvres. Set the cardboard to the marks on each side of the frame, and scribe the positions of the louvres on the inside of the frame. The frame is next pulled asunder and the trenches are formed about $\frac{1}{2}$ in. deep for the louvres, and then the frame is assembled permanently.

Preparing the Louvres. Draw a quarter of an ellipse, as shown in Fig. 97, by any convenient method. The following is the method of obtaining the axes of the ellipse: Set out a line R which is equal to the radius R in Fig. 96. Then draw a line at 45° to R, because the louvres are at 45° to the horizontal. Project ab on to the 45° line to $a'b'$, to give the semi-major axis of the ellipse. The semi-minor axis is equal to R, and is at right angles to $a'b'$. Complete the quarter-ellipse and cut out the shape for a templet.

The true shape of the end of every louvre will be some portion of the quarter-ellipse. Apply the templet to a groove in the frame, until a portion is found which fits the groove. Mark this portion and apply it to the end of the louvre intended for that particular groove. Repeat for each groove by finding which part of the templet fits the groove.

The bevels for the edge cut are found by placing a straight-edge across the frame and setting the bevel to the required shape. If the edges of the louvres are square, it is necessary to revolve the edge into the vertical plane to find the bevel. The principle is the same, as explained above, for finding the end of a louvre by the geometrical method.

ROOF LIGHTS

Lights may be formed in roofs by means of *skylights*, *dormers*, or *lantern lights*. Where light is not important, squares of glass may be substituted for slates, and special glass tiles may be obtained for tiled roofs.

Skylights. The simplest form of framed light is known as a skylight. It consists of a glazed frame lifted above the surface of the slates, but running

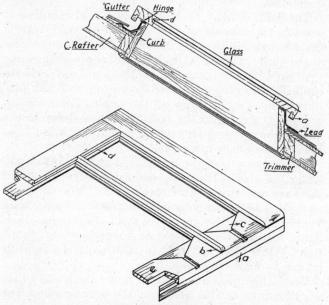

Fig. 98. Skylight

parallel to the roof surface. Fig. 98 shows a longitudinal section and an isometric view of the usual type of skylight.

Curb. The opening in the rafters is formed by two trimmers. The bottom one may be vertical, as in Fig. 98, or it may be at right angles to the surface, like the top trimmer. A *curb* is framed to the size of the opening and nailed to the rafters. The width of the curb depends upon the height of the sash above the roof. The bottom rail of the curb may be vertical, or at right angles to the roof surface, as are the sides and top of the curb. The sides are tongued into the top and bottom at the corners. In good-class work the corners are sometimes dovetailed.

The Sash, or light, rests on the curb, and is hinged at the top. It consists of two stiles, head, and bottom rail. Sometimes bars are included to decrease the sizes of the glass. The stiles, head, and bars are of the same thickness, but the bottom rail is the depth of the rebate thinner. The glass runs over the bottom rail, and projects about 1 in. to throw off the water. Condensation grooves C are cut in the bottom rail, as shown in the illustration. The sinkings also prevent the water from rising by capillary attraction.

Sometimes a *lead apron* is placed on the bottom rail under the glass. The lead passes under the rebates of the bars and stiles. This requires saw cuts, as shown at b. It is better to plough the head for the glass than to rebate it, as the groove is more watertight. Roof lights require special attention to make them watertight. Once they are fixed in position it is a difficult matter to make any alterations.

Protecting fillets a are mitred round the frame to act as throatings and to keep out the driving rain. The details of construction are shown in the isometric view. A barefaced tenon is used for the bottom rail, but an ordinary haunched tenon is used for the top rail.

Dormers. This form of roof light is generally intended as a feature in the design of the house. Usually, the sides are boarded and slated, or covered with lead. Fig. 99 shows a dormer with side-lights. The illustration shows a front elevation and a sectional end elevation on AB.

The opening in the roof is generally formed between

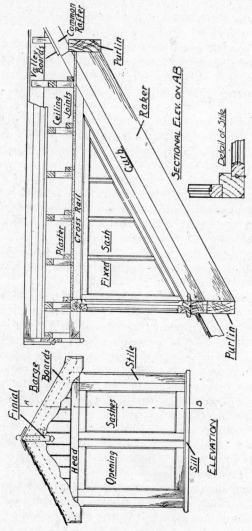

Fig. 99. DORMER LIGHT

Common Rafter

Valley Boards

Purlin

Ceiling Joists

Raker

Plaster

Cross Rail

Curb

Fixed Sash

SECTIONAL ELEV. ON AB

Detail of Stile

Purlin

Finial

Barge Boards

Stile

Head

Sashes

Opening

Sill

ELEVATION

two purlins. *Rakers* are framed between the purlins to carry the curb, which lifts the dormer above the roof surface so that gutters may be formed down the sides.

The side-heads, or cross-rails, run over the corner stiles, so that they can carry the projecting roof and barge boards. The front head is tenoned into the side-heads.

The details for the casements are the same as those already described. Every precaution must be taken in the construction to keep out the water. The front sashes are made to open ; they may open inwards or outwards. The former are difficult to make water-tight ; and the latter are dangerous, because of the exposed position, unless they are fixed securely when open. A mullion should be introduced if the dormer is wide. Usually, however, the opening sashes have a hook joint at the meeting stiles. The *spandrils*, or side sashes, are fixed. An enlarged detail is given separately in Fig. 99 for the corner stile.

The rafters, carrying the slates, run over the cross-rails to form projecting eaves. *Barge boards* are tenoned into the *finial*. Ceiling joists are thrown across the cross-rails to carry a lath and plaster ceiling. *Valley boards* are nailed on to the common rafters where the roof of the dormer dies away on to the main roof. The curb and raker are covered by a deep lining, which should be ploughed on the bottom edge to form a key for the ceiling plaster.

Very wide dormers usually have flat tops covered with lead. Mullions are used to divide the front into three or four lights. One casement is made to open, but the others are fixed.

Lantern Lights are used when side windows are not available. They are often used to light staircase wells and outbuildings attached to the main building. They are usually a feature of billiard rooms, because of the

advantage of the light coming from above, and also
for flat roofs.

The outline of the plan may be very varied. It may

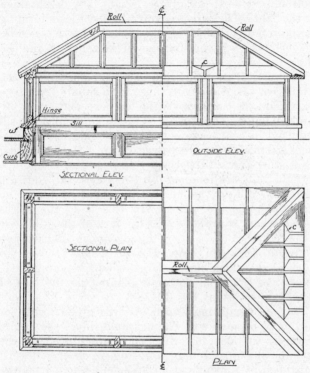

FIG. 100. LANTERN LIGHT

be rectangular, circular, or polygonal, and the outline
in elevation may be spherical, conical, or pyramidal.

Fig. 100 shows a lantern light with a rectangular
plan on a flat roof. The given views include elevation,
sectional elevation, plan, and sectional plan. The flat

roof is shown of wood, but it may be of steel or reinforced concrete. It is necessary to form a strong curb
to lift the sill of the light above the roof. A framed curb
is often used, so that a greater height may be obtained
for the light. The curb is covered by sheet lead, forming
an apron to the roof covering. If the roof is of concrete,
the curb may be a continuation of the concrete, and the
whole covered with asphalt.

The vertical framing requires no explanation, as the
details are very similar to those for a square bay. The
sill should be mitred at the corners and fixed by
handrail bolts. The stiles are stub tenoned into the sill
and fixed by coach screws. If the stiles are short, sometimes vertical bolts are passed down the stile, bolting
head, stile, and sill together.

If the rails are tenoned into the stiles, the ends are
mitred to obtain the maximum length of tenon, so
that they may be pinned. In this case, the sill is
mitred where it projects over the face of the stile.

Special precautions are required against condensation
falling into the room below. Fig. 101 *A* shows the section
of the sill, which has a large condensation groove.
Sometimes a special gutter is planted on the face of
the sill, as shown at Fig. 101 *B*.

The casements may open inwards or outwards, or
they may be pivoted. The example shows the sashes
arranged to open inwards. They are hinged at the
bottom, and operated by a system of cranked levers,
controlled by a handle at a convenient height from the
floor. If the sashes open outward, they are hinged at
the top. It is usual, in a light of this size, to have two
sashes arranged to open on each side. The casements
may be double rebated on the sides and top as a
greater precaution against the weather. Fig. 102 shows
the section through the corner stile.

The details for the roof lights are the same as for the

skylight. The chief difficulty is at the corners where the lights meet. The roof is formed of four frames. If they are mitred, as in Fig. 103, there is no difficulty except for finding the bevel. This is explained in " Geometry." It is a matter of finding the bisector of the dihedral angle. The bevel at the ridge is obtained directly from the vertical section.

If the hips and ridge are mitred, they should be ploughed to receive a loose tongue, so that they find their position easily when being erected. The joints

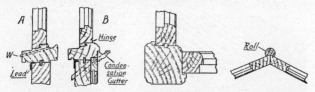

FIG. 101
DETAILS OF SILL

FIG. 102. SECTION
THROUGH STILE

FIG. 103. SECTION
THROUGH HIP

should be covered by *rolls*, which should be painted and bedded in white lead. Sometimes the ridge and hips are covered with sheet lead.

For large lights in better-class work, it is usual to have moulded and rebated hips and ridge. The lights lie in the rebates, and the timbers are covered with lead. Tingles are placed under the roll to hold down the lead. Condensation sinkings are made under each pane of glass, as shown in plan and outside elevation in Fig. 100.

Metal Lantern Light. Fig. 104 is an illustration of a metal lantern light for a reinforced concrete roof. The pivoted ventilators are operated by tension gearing. The top lights are glazed with patent glazing bars.

Glazing Bars. It is usual to have metal glazing bars for roof lights. They are stronger and more waterproof than wooden bars, and not so heavy in appearance.

There are many patent systems of roof glazing. Fig. 105 shows a section of Hope's patent glazing bar, as used on the lantern light shown in Fig. 104.

The galvanized steel bar, which is of " T "-section for strength, is covered with a lead sheath to prevent corrosion. An oiled asbestos cord is laid in a groove, and the glass rests on the cord. A lead sheath is turned

FIG. 104. METAL LANTERN LIGHT

down on the glass to make the joint watertight. Copper fixing shoes are used to fix the bars in position. If the water does penetrate, it is carried away by the channels under the glass, and condensation grooves are provided for the collection of moisture on the inside.

This form of glazing is more satisfactory than putty for roof lights. The asbestos cords are imperishable and form a dust-proof joint. Broken panes are easily replaced by turning back the lead capping, which is not liable to crack owing to the absence of angular bends.

Light Gearing. There are many different forms of casement openers for controlling lights in inaccessible positions. They are known as rotating shaft gearing, tension rod gearing, link gears, and twin-screw openers. In many cases they are used so that the light can be operated from the side of the window, to avoid having

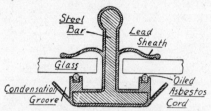

FIG. 105. GLAZING BAR

the cords hanging down the centre of the window. Fig. 106 shows a twin-screw opener operated by an endless cord at the side of the window. The operation

FIG. 106. TWIN-SCREW OPENER

of the cord controls the right- and left-hand nuts attached to the stays, which open or close the casement as required.

Tension Gearing. An elaborate system of tension gearing, made by H. Hope and Sons, is shown in Fig. 107.

The system operates a range of coupled ventilators
120 ft. long, by tension-rod gearing. The control is
operated at one end of the room, at floor level. It
can be worked by an endless chain, or by an electric
motor with automatic switch. This form of gearing is

Fig. 107. Tension Rod Gearing

now generally applied to large halls, where the ventilation is some height above the floor.

Ceiling Lights, or lay-lights, are sashes ornamented
by bars and fixed in the ceiling. The ceiling joists are
trimmed, and rebated linings are mitred round the
opening to carry the sash. Lay lights, which are also
called *borrowed lights*, because they receive the light

from other windows, are generally used to hide the open roof containing the roof light.

Fig. 108 shows a lay-light ornamented by bars. The sash is prepared in the ordinary way. The bars may

HORIZONTAL SECTION

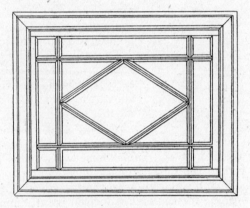

INVERTED PLAN

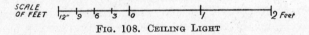

SCALE OF FEET

FIG. 108. CEILING LIGHT

be varied in many ways. An elliptical arrangement at the centre is very often used in place of the diamond- or lozenge-shaped panel in Fig. 108. The bars forming the margin should be halved where they intersect, and they should be tenoned into the rails of the sash.

The central part forming the ornamentation must be securely fastened to the marginal bars. The simplest method is to prepare the central bars, shown in Fig. 108, separately, making the mitres secure by dowels or slip feathers. When the bars are fitted in position they should be screwed or dowelled to the bars forming the margin. If the central panel were elliptical, it would be detached from the margin and supported by four short bars. The short bars would be tenoned into the margin and into the central panel. The elliptical bars could be cut from the solid and the joints made

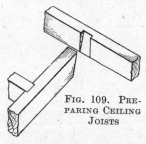

FIG. 109. PRE-PARING CEILING JOISTS

secure with dowels. These sashes are not exposed to the weather, and glue may be used to secure the joints.

The sash is usually glazed with ornamental glass, so as to screen the roof timbers above the light. If the bars are not sufficiently strong to carry the glass, metal bars may be screwed across the frame and into the edges of the rebates of the bars. Sometimes metal plates are shaped to the outline of the rebates at the joints of the bars, and screwed on to the top edges.

The opening for the sash is formed by trimming the ceiling joists to the required sizes. Usually a bevelled housing secured by nails, as shown in Fig. 109, is satisfactory, especially for old work. If the sash is very heavy and the ceiling joists are being prepared in new work, the joists should be prepared in the same way as for a floor.

The rebate is formed by planting 1 in. margin pieces round the opening. Fig. 108 shows an architrave mitred round, to cover the joint between the plaster and the planted rebate. Usually, however, the pieces forming the rebate are moulded on the inside corner and ploughed on the back to form a key for the plaster.

INDEX

SECTION V

DOORS, FRAMES, AND PANELLING

SECTION VI
GEOMETRY

SECTION VII

WINDOWS

END OF VOLUME II